First published 2016 by
Elmwood Education
Unit 5, Mallow Park
Watchmead
Welwyn Garden City
Herts. AL7 1GX
Tel. 01707 333 232

ISBN 9781 906 622 626

Typeset and illustrated by Tech-Set Ltd., Gateshead, Tyne and Wear.

PREFACE

Target your Maths has been written for pupils in Year 2 and their teachers.

The intention of this workbook is to provide teachers with material to teach the statutory requirements set out in the Year 2 Programme of Study for Mathematics in the renewed 2014 National Curriculum Framework. The Programme of Study Guide matches the statutory requirements with the relevant page or pages.

Each page is divided into three sections.

- Section A: activities based upon work previously covered. This section generally matches the requirements for Year 1 pupils. It can be used to remind children of work previously covered, as well as providing material for the less confident child.

- Section B: activities based upon the requirements for Year 2 pupils. Most children should be able to work successfully at this level.

- Section C: activities providing extension material for the faster workers and for those who need to be moved quickly onto more challenging tasks. The work in this section generally matches the requirements for the Year 3 pupils. Problems in Section C can also provide useful material for discussion in the plenary session.

- The correspondence of the three sections A–C to the requirements for different year groups provides a simple, manageable structure for planning differentiated activities and for both formal and informal assessment of children's progress. The commonality of the content pitched at different levels also allows for progression within the lesson. Children acquiring confidence at one level find they can successfully complete activities at the next level.

Target your Maths has been organised into a three term school year. Each term there are activities covering statutory requirements in each of the seven domains in the renewed Framework. The Number and Measurement domains are revisited within each term, whereas Fractions, Geometry and Statistics are dealt with as discrete topics. There is, of course, no set path through either the Year 2 Programme of Study or Target your Maths but teachers may find the approach used in this workbook useful for planning purposes.

The author is indebted to many colleagues who have assisted him in this work. He is particularly grateful to Sharon Granville and Davina Tunkel for their invaluable advice and assistance.

Stephen Pearce

Year 2 NC Programme of Study Guide

NUMBER AND PLACE VALUE

1, 47, 64, 81	count in steps of 2, 3 and 5 from 0, and in tens from any number, forward and backward
2	recognise the place value of each digit in a two-digit number (tens, ones)
46, 82	identify, represent and estimate numbers using different representations, including the number line
3, 33	compare and order numbers from 0 up to 100; use $<$, $>$ and $=$ signs
32	read and write numbers to at least 100 in numerals and in words
65	use place value and number facts to solve problems.

ADDITION AND SUBTRACTION

Solve problems with addition and subtraction:

55, 56, 74, 90	using concrete objects and pictorial representations, including those involving numbers, quantities and measures
4, 11, 35, 40, 68, 73	applying their increasing knowledge of mental and written methods
24, 53	recall and use addition and subtraction facts to 20 fluently, and derive and use related facts up to 100
	add and subtract numbers using concrete objects, pictorial representations, and mentally, including:
5, 10, 34, 39	a two-digit number and ones
66, 72	a two-digit number and tens
6, 41	two two-digit numbers
26, 67	adding three one-digit numbers
25	show that addition of two numbers can be done in any order (commutative) and subtraction of one number from another cannot
54, 88, 89	recognise and use the inverse relationship between addition and subtraction and use this to check calculations and solve missing number problems.

MULTIPLICATION AND DIVISION

21, 22, 29, 48, 49, 83, 95	recall and use multiplication and division facts for the 2, 5 and 10 multiplication tables, including recognising odd and even numbers
60	calculate mathematical statements for multiplication and division within the multiplication tables and write them using the multiplication ($\times$), division ($\div$) and equals ($=$) signs
59, 84, 93	show that multiplication of two numbers can be done in any order (commutative) and division of one number by another cannot
19, 20, 61, 94	solve problems involving multiplication and division, using materials, arrays, repeated addition, mental methods, and multiplication and division facts, including problems in contexts.

FRACTIONS

23, 50, 51, 85, 86	recognise, find, name and write fractions $\frac{1}{3}$, $\frac{1}{4}$, $\frac{2}{4}$ and $\frac{3}{4}$ of a length, shape, set of objects or quantity
50, 51, 86, 87	write simple fractions for example, $\frac{1}{2}$ of 6 = 3 and recognise the equivalence of $\frac{2}{4}$ and $\frac{1}{2}$.

MEASUREMENT

7–9, 37, 38, 69, 70	choose and use appropriate standard units to estimate and measure length/height in any direction (m/cm); mass (kg/g); temperatures (°C); capacity (litres/ml) to the nearest appropriate unit, using rulers, scales, thermometers and measuring vessels
71	compare and order lengths, mass, volume/capacity and record the results $>$, $<$ and $=$
13, 42	recognise and use symbols for pounds (£) and pence (p); combine amounts to make a particular value
42, 75	find different combinations of coins that equal the same amounts of money
14, 76	solve simple problems in a practical context involving addition and subtraction of money of the same unit, including giving change
63	compare and sequence intervals of time
30, 62, 96	tell and write the time to five minutes, including quarter past/to the hour and draw the hands on a clock face to show these times
31	know the number of minutes in an hour and the number of hours in a day.

GEOMETRY

15–17	identify and describe the properties of 2-D shapes, including the number of sides and line symmetry in a vertical line
43	identify and describe the properties of 3-D shapes, including the number of edges, vertices and faces
44	identify 2-D shapes on the surface of 3-D shapes, [for example, a circle on a cylinder and a triangle on a pyramid]
45	compare and sort common 2-D and 3-D shapes and everyday objects
18	order and arrange combinations of mathematical objects in patterns and sequences
77–80	use mathematical vocabulary to describe position, direction and movement, including movement in a straight line and distinguishing between rotation as a turn and in terms of right angles for quarter, half and three-quarter turns (clockwise and anti-clockwise).

STATISTICS

27, 28, 57, 58, 91, 92	interpret and construct simple pictograms, tally charts, block diagrams and simple tables
27, 28, 57, 58, 91, 92	ask and answer simple questions by counting the number of objects in each category and sorting the categories by quantity
27, 28, 57, 58, 91, 92	ask and answer questions about totalling and comparing categorical data.

Year 2

CONTENTS

A

Fill in the boxes.

2   4   6   [ ] [ ]

14   16   18   [ ] [ ]

8   10   12   [ ] [ ]

16   18   20   [ ] [ ]

12   14   16   [ ] [ ]

Count on.

4 twos from 0   [8]

5 twos from 4   [ ]

4 twos from 14   [ ]

6 twos from 6   [ ]

5 twos from 10   [ ]

Count on.

4 twos from 8   [ ]

5 twos from 12   [ ]

3 twos from 18   [ ]

6 twos from 2   [ ]

4 twos from 16   [ ]

B

Fill in the boxes.

28   30   32   [ ] [ ]

18   16   14   [ ] [ ]

52   54   56   [ ] [ ]

30   28   26   [ ] [ ]

76   78   80   [ ] [ ]

Count on.

3 twos from 38   [ ]

7 twos from 62   [ ]

6 twos from 86   [ ]

5 twos from 20   [ ]

4 twos from 44   [ ]

Count back.

5 twos from 36   [ ]

4 twos from 72   [ ]

6 twos from 58   [ ]

3 twos from 24   [ ]

4 twos from 100   [ ]

C

Count on.

6 twos from 376   [ ]

8 twos from 140   [ ]

7 twos from 794   [ ]

9 twos from 218   [ ]

5 twos from 952   [ ]

Count back.

4 twos from 124   [ ]

6 twos from 480   [ ]

9 twos from 548   [ ]

5 twos from 806   [ ]

7 twos from 312   [ ]

How many twos?

94 to 106   [6]

88 to 104   [ ]

90 to 112   [ ]

92 to 102   [ ]

98 to 116   [ ]

A

Fill in the boxes.

16 = [10] + 6

83 = 80 + [ ]

57 = [ ] + 7

24 = 20 + [ ]

69 = [ ] + 9

48 = 40 + [ ]

91 = [ ] + 1

35 = 30 + [ ]

76 = [ ] + 6

54 = 50 + [ ]

28 = [ ] + 8

85 = 80 + [ ]

62 = [ ] + 2

43 = 40 + [ ]

97 = [ ] + 7

B

Write the value of the underlined digit?

3 9̲   [9]

7̲ 3   [ ]

9̲ 8   [ ]

6 5̲   [ ]

2̲ 6   [ ]

8 2̲   [ ]

5̲ 9   [ ]

4 7̲   [ ]

9 4̲   [ ]

3̲ 2   [ ]

2̲ 1   [ ]

7 5̲   [ ]

6̲ 3   [ ]

4̲ 2   [ ]

8 6̲   [ ]

C

Write the value of the underlined digit?.

3 1̲ 9   [ ]

2̲ 3 7   [ ]

9 7̲ 0   [ ]

5 4 8̲   [ ]

1 6̲ 5   [ ]

6̲ 8 4   [ ]

8 5 2̲   [ ]

7̲ 0 6   [ ]

2 9̲ 3   [ ]

9̲ 2 7   [ ]

4 7 5̲   [ ]

8 4̲ 9   [ ]

2̲ 8 1   [ ]

5 3 4̲   [ ]

3 5̲ 6   [ ]

A Colour the larger number.   Colour the smaller number.

(17)   or   (14) | (31)   or   (13)   (47)   or   (54) | (52)   or   (25)

(26)   or   (19) | (23)   or   (29)   (86)   or   (85) | (28)   or   (31)

(59)   or   (61) | (75)   or   (82)   (91)   or   (79) | (43)   or   (39)

(68)   or   (82) | (13)   or   (9)   (34)   or   (40) | (79)   or   (80)

B Write > or < in the box.

61 [ ] 59 | 25 [ ] 23 | 69 [ ] 71 | 56 [ ] 55

99 [ ] 100 | 36 [ ] 34 | 74 [ ] 82 | 85 [ ] 86

53 [ ] 35 | 87 [ ] 89 | 93 [ ] 100 | 48 [ ] 50

78 [ ] 87 | 42 [ ] 39 | 21 [ ] 19 | 60 [ ] 59

C Write > or < in the box.

283 [ ] 238 | 158 [ ] 185 | 246 [ ] 264 | 927 [ ] 909

319 [ ] 321 | 724 [ ] 472 | 362 [ ] 266 | 584 [ ] 548

970 [ ] 799 | 697 [ ] 719 | 139 [ ] 93 | 455 [ ] 545

835 [ ] 855 | 503 [ ] 350 | 672 [ ] 726 | 806 [ ] 840

Find the sum of each pair of numbers.

A

10 and 8 [18]

7 and 9 [ ]

12 and 5 [ ]

3 and 15 [ ]

7 and 6 [ ]

12 and 8 [ ]

5 and 9 [ ]

4 and 11 [ ]

20 and 10 [ ]

50 and 10 [ ]

10 and 90 [ ]

10 and 40 [ ]

76 and 10 [ ]

34 and 10 [ ]

10 and 89 [ ]

10 and 62 [ ]

B

7 and 36 [ ]

88 and 4 [ ]

6 and 19 [ ]

62 and 9 [ ]

5 and 37 [ ]

45 and 8 [ ]

3 and 79 [ ]

58 and 7 [ ]

40 and 30 [ ]

50 and 50 [ ]

20 and 70 [ ]

60 and 40 [ ]

70 and 23 [ ]

20 and 58 [ ]

45 and 40 [ ]

61 and 30 [ ]

C

9 and 416 [ ]

5 and 749 [ ]

397 and 8 [ ]

178 and 6 [ ]

4 and 809 [ ]

9 and 628 [ ]

257 and 7 [ ]

534 and 8 [ ]

70 and 360 [ ]

40 and 680 [ ]

420 and 90 [ ]

590 and 60 [ ]

80 and 182 [ ]

50 and 894 [ ]

247 and 70 [ ]

735 and 90 [ ]

Fill in the boxes.

A

15 + 2 = 10 + ☐ 7 = ☐ 17   13 + 5 = ☐ 18   17 + 3 = ☐

12 + 6 = 10 + ☐ = ☐   15 + 4 = ☐   13 + 2 = ☐

11 + 9 = 10 + ☐ = ☐   11 + 6 = ☐   12 + 8 = ☐

16 + 3 = 10 + ☐ = ☐   14 + 1 = ☐   14 + 5 = ☐

14 + 4 = 10 + ☐ = ☐   12 + 2 = ☐   11 + 3 = ☐

B

17 + 9 ☐   19 + 6 ☐   15 + 7 ☐   18 + 9 ☐

15 + 6 ☐   16 + 7 ☐   18 + 6 ☐   17 + 4 ☐

19 + 4 ☐   13 + 8 ☐   19 + 9 ☐   15 + 8 ☐

16 + 9 ☐   18 + 3 ☐   12 + 9 ☐   16 + 6 ☐

18 + 5 ☐   15 + 9 ☐   17 + 7 ☐   14 + 9 ☐

14 + 7 ☐   17 + 8 ☐   16 + 8 ☐   18 + 7 ☐

C

38 + 7 ☐   47 + 8 ☐   69 + 5 ☐   96 + 8 ☐

64 + 8 ☐   83 + 7 ☐   76 + 6 ☐   45 + 6 ☐

57 + 6 ☐   29 + 8 ☐   24 + 7 ☐   28 + 9 ☐

75 + 9 ☐   66 + 9 ☐   98 + 4 ☐   99 + 7 ☐

26 + 7 ☐   95 + 7 ☐   37 + 9 ☐   63 + 9 ☐

39 + 3 ☐   58 + 8 ☐   52 + 9 ☐   87 + 5 ☐

Examples

```
    3 5              3 5                   3 5
  + 2 3            + 2 9                 + 2 9            5 + 9 = 14
        8  Add units    1 4                 6 4  ←——— 4 in units column
    5 0  Add tens       5 0                   1  ←——— 10 is carried into tens (1)
    5 8  Find total     6 4
```

Use the above examples. Set out in columns and work out.

A

```
    1 3           1 2
  + 1 2         + 1 7
  .......        ..........
      5
    2 0
  _____        _____
  _____        _____
```

```
    2 6           2 4
  + 1 3         + 2 4
  .........      .........
  _____        _____
  _____        _____
```

```
    3 1           4 5
  + 1 8         + 1 4
  .........      .........
  _____        _____
  _____        _____
```

```
    5 1           3 7
  + 1 7         + 2 0
  ..........     .........
  _____        _____
  _____        _____
```

B

```
    3 5           4 6
  + 2 8         + 2 7
  ..........     ..........
  _____        _____
  _____        _____
```

```
    3 7           5 6
  + 3 4         + 2 5
  ..........     ..........
  _____        _____
  _____        _____
```

```
    5 8           4 9
  + 1 9         + 3 4
  ..........     ..........
  _____        _____
  _____        _____
```

```
    6 9           2 7
  + 2 6         + 2 7
  ..........     ..........
  _____        _____
  _____        _____
```

C

```
    4 9           5 7
  + 3 3         + 2 6
  _____        _____

    3 8           7 4
  + 1 7         + 1 8
  _____        _____
```

```
    5 5           4 9
  + 3 5         + 2 5
  _____        _____
```

```
    6 7           3 4
  + 1 8         + 3 6
  _____        _____

    3 6           6 3
  + 2 9         + 2 8
  _____        _____
```

```
    3 9           4 6
  + 2 8         + 1 5
  _____        _____
```

A

Write m or cm in the box.

car	m	house		brick	
key		book		road	
fish		playground		hand	
tree		can		wall	

B

Colour the most sensible estimate.

length of classroom

(1 m)   (100 m)
(10 m)

finger length

(5 cm)   (15 cm)
(10 cm)

football pitch

(1 m)   (100 m)
(10 m)

height of mug

(10 cm)   (10 m)
(1 m)

door height

(50 cm)   (200 cm)
(100 cm)

skipping rope

(20 cm)   (20 m)
(2 m)

C

Choose the most sensible units. Write mm, cm, m or km in the box.

a fence		a bottle		a boat	
a chair		a coach trip		a counter	
England		a smartie		an arm	
an ant		a pond		a river	

Fill in the boxes.

 A

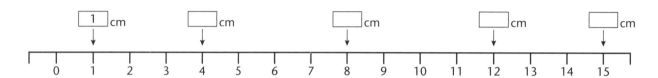

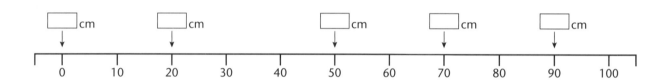

 B

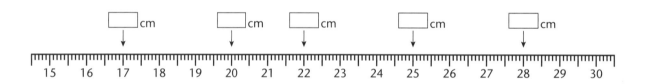

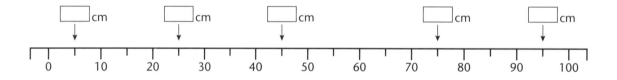

C

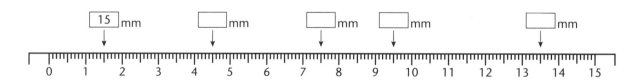

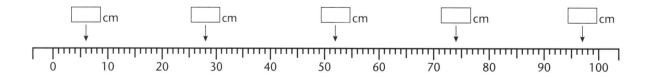

A

Measure these lines to the nearest centimetre.

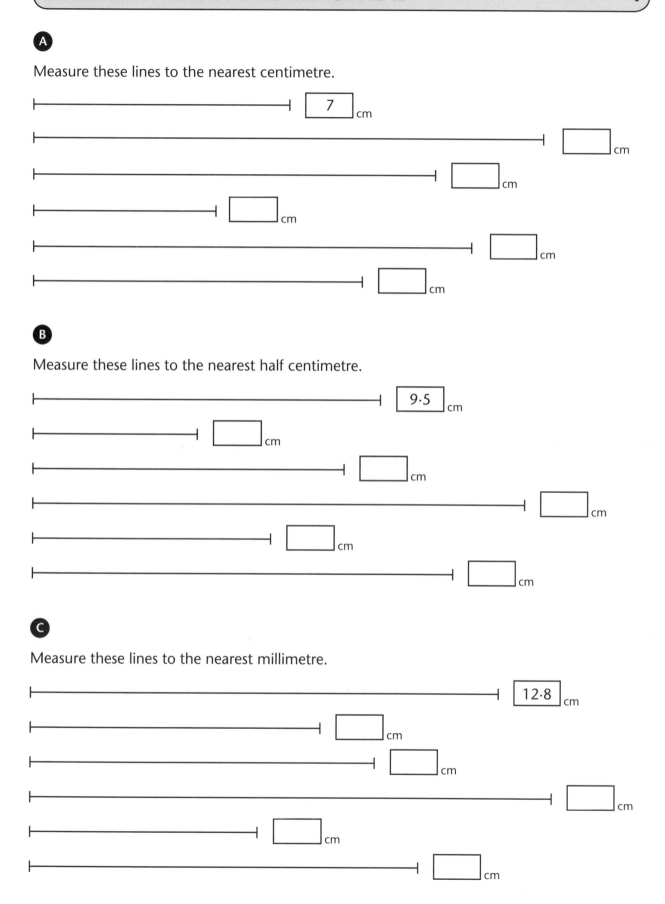

B

Measure these lines to the nearest half centimetre.

C

Measure these lines to the nearest millimetre.

Fill in the boxes.

A

13 − 6 = **7**	16 − 5	11 − 6	16 − 8
20 − 11	13 − 9	13 − 8	14 − 5
11 − 3	17 − 8	18 − 9	11 − 9
14 − 7	14 − 9	12 − 5	17 − 4
12 − 8	19 − 5	20 − 7	12 − 3

B

21 − 7	23 − 9	24 − 5	21 − 8
28 − 3	27 − 6	21 − 4	23 − 7
23 − 4	30 − 8	26 − 7	30 − 5
26 − 9	24 − 7	29 − 9	27 − 9
22 − 8	22 − 4	25 − 8	24 − 8
25 − 7	28 − 9	22 − 3	25 − 6

C

70 − 4	32 − 7	88 − 7	84 − 9
53 − 8	46 − 9	63 − 9	31 − 3
34 − 6	74 − 8	92 − 5	79 − 5
61 − 5	93 − 6	66 − 8	43 − 4
95 − 9	51 − 9	45 − 6	80 − 6
87 − 8	65 − 7	30 − 9	52 − 9

Find the difference between each pair of numbers.

A   **B**   **C**

7 and 11 → 4	57 and 8	183 and 5
15 and 8	60 and 90	671 and 8
10 and 100	9 and 74	213 and 6
18 and 9	83 and 7	40 and 502
17 and 20	69 and 50	800 and 2
14 and 6	31 and 5	29 and 16
16 and 7	7 and 84	90 and 278
80 and 10	92 and 4	320 and 50
19 and 12	53 and 20	854 and 6
10 and 40	81 and 5	9 and 497
8 and 17	30 and 87	80 and 136
12 and 6	7 and 52	712 and 8
13 and 18	9 and 63	4 and 591
60 and 10	24 and 5	5 and 170
4 and 13	45 and 8	743 and 60
20 and 6	70 and 95	8 and 434

Examples

```
   5 6                      5 6                        ⁴5̸ ¹6   6 − 8
 − 2 4                    − 2 4   (6 − 4 = 2)        − 2 8   Borrow 10 (⁴5̸ ¹6)
 ─────                    ─────                       ─────
     2   (6 − 4 = 2)       3 2   (50 − 20 = 30)        2 8   16 − 8 = 8
 ........                                                     40 − 20 = 20
   3 0   (50 − 20 = 30)
 ─────
   3 2   Total
 ─────
```

Use the above examples. Set out in columns.

A

```
   2 8        3 7
 − 1 5      − 2 4
 ─────
     3
 ........
   1 0
 ─────      ─────


   3 5        5 9
 − 1 3      − 1 7
 ........    ........
 ─────      ─────
 ─────      ─────


   5 6        4 6
 − 2 1      − 2 5
 ........    ........
 ─────      ─────
 ─────      ─────


   4 4        5 3
 − 1 4      − 3 0
 ........    ........
 ─────      ─────
 ─────      ─────
```

B

```
   5 7        7 6
 − 4 3      − 5 2
 ─────
   1 4
 ─────

   8 5        5 8
 − 5 2      − 2 3
 ─────      ─────


   7 9        8 7
 − 2 7      − 2 0
 ─────      ─────


   9 8        9 6
 − 4 8      − 5 4
 ─────      ─────


   6 4        6 9
 − 2 3      − 4 6
 ─────      ─────


   4 9        7 3
 − 2 5      − 3 3
 ─────      ─────
```

C

```
  ⁵6̸ ¹6       7 1
 − 3 9      − 3 9
 ─────      ─────


   9 0        6 2
 − 6 1      − 5 7
 ─────      ─────


   7 4        8 0
 − 1 8      − 6 6
 ─────      ─────


   5 2        9 7
 − 3 4      − 3 8
 ─────      ─────


   8 3        5 5
 − 3 9      − 2 9
 ─────      ─────


   9 3        4 3
 − 7 6      − 2 7
 ─────      ─────
```

A

Write the amount.

  25 p   ☐ p   ☐ p

  ☐ p   ☐ p   ☐ p

  ☐ p   ☐ p   ☐ p

B

Make the amounts. Use the number of notes and coins shown.

£25 £10 ☐ ☐   £10·70 ☐ ◯ ◯

£40 ☐ ☐ ☐   £21·50 ☐ ◯ ◯

£35 ☐ ☐ ☐   £7·05 ☐ ◯ ◯

C

Make the amounts. Use the number of notes and coins shown.

£30·25 ☐ ☐ ◯ ◯   £10·56 ☐ ◯ ◯ ◯

£15·60 ☐ ☐ ◯ ◯   £5·45 ☐ ◯ ◯ ◯

£25·11 ☐ ☐ ◯ ◯   £20·17 ☐ ◯ ◯ ◯

Fill in the boxes.

A

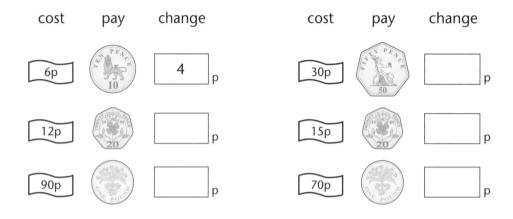

cost	pay	change		cost	pay	change
6p	TEN PENCE 10	4 p		30p	FIFTY PENCE 50	p
12p	20	p		15p	20	p
90p	ONE POUND	p		70p	ONE POUND	p

B

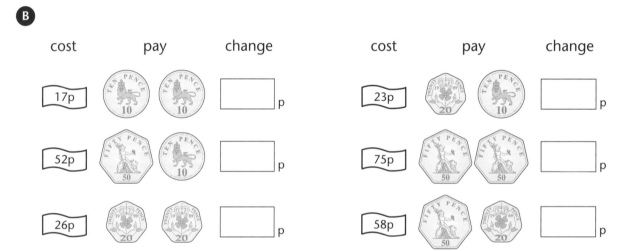

cost	pay	change		cost	pay	change
17p	TEN PENCE 10 TEN PENCE 10	p		23p	20 TEN PENCE 10	p
52p	FIFTY PENCE 50 TEN PENCE 10	p		75p	FIFTY PENCE 50 FIFTY PENCE 50	p
26p	20 20	p		58p	FIFTY PENCE 50 20	p

C

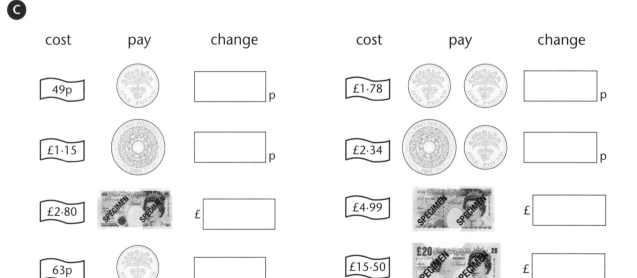

cost	pay	change		cost	pay	change
49p	ONE POUND	p		£1·78	ONE POUND ONE POUND	p
£1·15	TWO POUNDS	p		£2·34	TWO POUNDS ONE POUND	p
£2·80	SPECIMEN	£		£4·99	SPECIMEN	£
63p	ONE POUND	p		£15·50	£20 SPECIMEN SPECIMEN	£

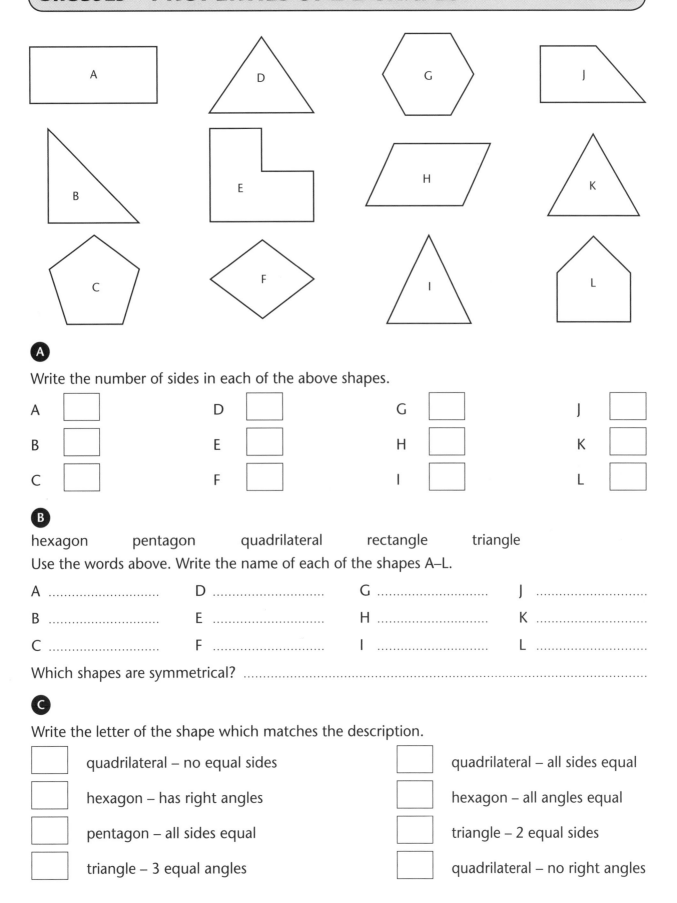

A

Write the number of sides in each of the above shapes.

A ☐   D ☐   G ☐   J ☐

B ☐   E ☐   H ☐   K ☐

C ☐   F ☐   I ☐   L ☐

B

hexagon   pentagon   quadrilateral   rectangle   triangle

Use the words above. Write the name of each of the shapes A–L.

A ....   D ....   G ....   J ....

B ....   E ....   H ....   K ....

C ....   F ....   I ....   L ....

Which shapes are symmetrical? ....

C

Write the letter of the shape which matches the description.

☐   quadrilateral – no equal sides   ☐   quadrilateral – all sides equal

☐   hexagon – has right angles   ☐   hexagon – all angles equal

☐   pentagon – all sides equal   ☐   triangle – 2 equal sides

☐   triangle – 3 equal angles   ☐   quadrilateral – no right angles

A

Use a ruler.

Draw one line of symmetry.

B

Complete the symmetrical shapes.

C

Use a ruler.

Draw on 2 lines of symmetry.

Complete the shape.

Draw on another line of symmetry.

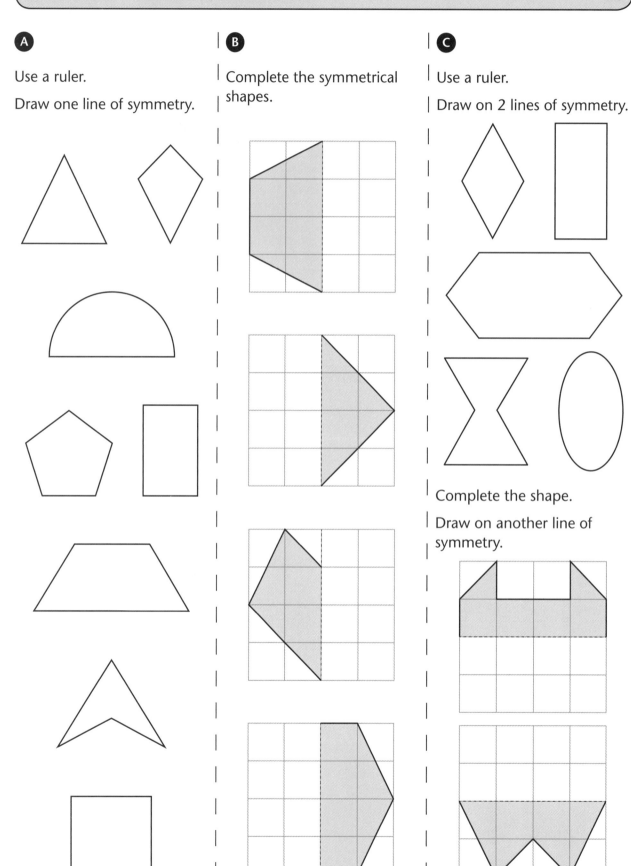

A

Use a ruler.

Draw these shapes using the grid lines.

rectangle
sides 4 cm, 2 cm

square
sides 3 cm

rectangle
sides 4 cm × 3 cm

B

Use a set square or page corner to draw quarter turns.

Draw these shapes.

rectangle 5 cm by 3 cm

square 4 cm by 4 cm

rectangle 2 cm by 6 cm

C

Draw these shapes accurately.

rectangle
4·5 cm by 5·5 cm

square
3·5 cm by 3·5 cm

rectangle
5·5 cm by 2·5 cm

Colour the shapes red (R), blue (B), green (G) or yellow (Y).

A

Finish colouring in these patterns

Ⓡ Ⓡ ☐B Ⓡ Ⓡ ☐B Ⓡ Ⓡ ☐ ◯ ◯ ☐ ◯ ◯ ☐

△Y △R △Y Ⓡ Ⓡ △Y △R △Y ◯ ◯ △ △ △ ◯ ◯

Ⓑ △Y ☐B ☐Y ☐B △Y ☐B ☐Y ◯ △ ☐ ☐ ◯ △ ☐ ☐

B

Colour in these patterns.

☐R Ⓡ ☐G Ⓖ ☐R Ⓡ ☐ ◯ ☐ ◯

△Y △B ☐Y ☐B ☐Y △B △ ☐ ☐ ☐

Ⓖ △Y △G Ⓨ △G △Y ◯ △ △ ◯

Draw and colour shape:

12 ☐   17 ☐   21 ☐

15 ☐   21 ☐   34 ☐

12 ☐   16 ☐   31 ☐

C

Fill the grid with the pattern.

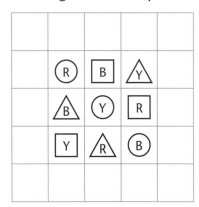

Colour in this pattern.

Ⓡ Ⓨ ☐R Ⓨ Ⓡ ☐Y

Draw and colour shape:

9 ☐   16 ☐   23 ☐

32 ☐   43 ☐   60 ☐

A

Group the dots.
Fill in the boxes.

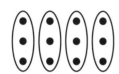

$3 + 3 + 3 + 3 = \boxed{}$

$4 \times 3 = \boxed{}$

$6 + 6 = \boxed{}$

$2 \times 6 = \boxed{}$

$4 + 4 + 4 + 4 + 4 = \boxed{}$

$5 \times 4 = \boxed{}$

$10 + 10 + 10 = \boxed{}$

$3 \times 10 = \boxed{}$

B

Group the dots.
Fill in the boxes.

three 7s = $\boxed{}$

$3 \times 7 = \boxed{}$

two 8s = $\boxed{}$

$2 \times 8 = \boxed{}$

five 9s = $\boxed{}$

$5 \times 9 = \boxed{}$

eight 3s = $\boxed{}$

$8 \times 3 = \boxed{}$

C

Draw the dots.
Fill in the boxes.

eight 5s = $\boxed{}$

$8 \times 5 = \boxed{}$

two 11s = $\boxed{}$

$2 \times 11 = \boxed{}$

seven 4s = $\boxed{}$

$7 \times 4 = \boxed{}$

three 9s = $\boxed{}$

$3 \times 9 = \boxed{}$

Group the dots. Counts the groups. Fill in the boxes.

A

Group in 3s.

$\boxed{15} \div 3 = \boxed{5}$

Group in 5s.

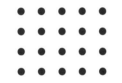

$\boxed{} \div 5 = \boxed{}$

Group in 2s.

$\boxed{} \div 2 = \boxed{}$

Group in 4s.

$\boxed{} \div 4 = \boxed{}$

B

Group in 2s.

$\boxed{} \div 2 = \boxed{}$

Group in 3s.

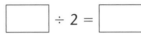

$\boxed{} \div 3 = \boxed{}$

Group in 4s.

$\boxed{} \div 4 = \boxed{}$

Group in 6s.

$\boxed{} \div 6 = \boxed{}$

C

Fill in the boxes.

40 counters.

$\boxed{}$ groups of 2

$\boxed{}$ groups of 5

$\boxed{}$ groups of 10

$\boxed{}$ groups of 20

$\boxed{}$ groups of 8

24 books

$\boxed{}$ piles of 2

$\boxed{}$ piles of 3

$\boxed{}$ piles of 4

$\boxed{}$ piles of 6

$\boxed{}$ piles of 8

60p

$\boxed{}$ 2ps

$\boxed{}$ 5ps

$\boxed{}$ 10ps

$\boxed{}$ 20ps

$\boxed{}$ 1ps

£1

$\boxed{}$ 50ps

$\boxed{}$ 20ps

$\boxed{}$ 10ps

$\boxed{}$ 5ps

$\boxed{}$ 2ps

Colour the 2 times table.

1	2	3	4	5	6	7	8	9	10	11	12
13	14	15	16	17	18	19	20	21	22	23	24

2 Times Table | 2 | 4 | | | | | | | | | | |

B

3 × 2	6	12 × 2		10 ÷ 2	5	14 ÷ 2	
10 × 2		1 × 2		22 ÷ 2		20 ÷ 2	
9 × 2		8 × 2		12 ÷ 2		4 ÷ 2	
5 × 2		6 × 2		2 ÷ 2		24 ÷ 2	
2 × 2		11 × 2		18 ÷ 2		8 ÷ 2	
7 × 2		4 × 2		6 ÷ 2		16 ÷ 2	

C

6	× 2 = 18		× 2 = 8		÷ 2 = 7		÷ 2 = 1
	× 2 = 4		× 2 = 20		÷ 2 = 4		÷ 2 = 8
	× 2 = 14		× 2 = 16		÷ 2 = 11		÷ 2 = 3
	× 2 = 24		× 2 = 12		÷ 2 = 2		÷ 2 = 5
	× 2 = 10		× 2 = 6		÷ 2 = 6		÷ 2 = 12
	× 2 = 2		× 2 = 22		÷ 2 = 10		÷ 2 = 9

A

Colour the numbers.
odd – red
even – yellow

1	11
2	12
3	13
4	14
5	15
6	16
7	17
8	18
9	19
10	20

Fill in the boxes.

Odd	Even
1	☐
3	4
☐	☐
☐	8
9	☐
☐	☐
☐	14
☐	☐
17	18
☐	☐

B

Colour the numbers.
odd – red
even – yellow

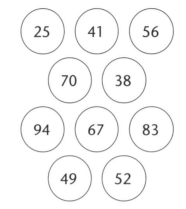

Odd numbers end with

...1..., ...3..., ..., ... or ....

Even numbers end with

........, ..., ..., ... or ....

Fill in the boxes.

☐	31
52	☐
54	☐
☐	37
☐	☐
60	☐
☐	☐
66	☐
☐	49

C

Colour the numbers.
odd – red
even – yellow

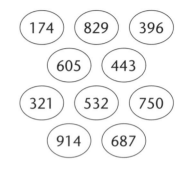

What is the next odd
number after:

25	☐	136	☐
18	☐	570	☐
81	☐	243	☐
52	☐	394	☐
67	☐	409	☐
59	☐	800	☐

What is the next even
number after:

83	☐	175	☐
10	☐	429	☐
47	☐	374	☐
92	☐	601	☐
65	☐	938	☐
79	☐	199	☐

A

Divide each lines into halves. Write $\frac{1}{2}$ at the halfway mark.

$\frac{1}{2}$

0 ———————————— 1   0 ———————————— 1

0 ———————————— 1   0 ———————————— 1

0 ———————————— 1   0 ———————————— 1

B

Divide each line into quarters. Label your marks $\frac{1}{4}, \frac{2}{4}, \frac{3}{4}$.

0 ———————————— 1   0 ———————————— 1

0 ———————————— 1   0 ———————————— 1

Divide each line into thirds. Label your marks $\frac{1}{3}, \frac{2}{3}$.

0 ———————————— 1   0 ———————————— 1

0 ———————————— 1   0 ———————————— 1

C

Find one half of:		Find one third of:		Find one quarter of:	
16 cm	cm	15 cm	cm	20 cm	cm
20 cm	cm	36 m	m	32 m	m
50 cm	cm	600 m	m	100 m	m
400 m	m	24 cm	cm	48 cm	cm
1 m	cm	30 m	m	600 m	m

Fill in the boxes.

A

9 + 6 = `15`

5 + 7 = `___`

12 + 8 = `___`

8 + 5 = `___`

7 + 9 = `___`

4 + 8 = `___`

6 + 7 = `___`

11 + 6 = `___`

15 − 7 = `___`

17 − 5 = `___`

20 − 11 = `___`

12 − 5 = `___`

13 − 9 = `___`

20 − 17 = `___`

14 − 8 = `___`

20 − 6 = `___`

B

80 + 20 = `___`

50 + 30 = `___`

30 + 40 = `___`

60 + 30 = `___`

40 + 60 = `___`

70 + 20 = `___`

10 + 70 = `___`

20 + 40 = `___`

90 − 20 = `___`

60 − 50 = `___`

100 − 40 = `___`

50 − 30 = `___`

70 − 40 = `___`

80 − 60 = `___`

40 − 10 = `___`

100 − 90 = `___`

C

90 + 80 = `___`

70 + 40 = `___`

60 + 90 = `___`

80 + 30 = `___`

500 + 500 = `___`

500 + 200 = `___`

400 + 600 = `___`

100 + 500 = `___`

160 − 30 = `___`

130 − 50 = `___`

110 − 60 = `___`

140 − 70 = `___`

700 − 500 = `___`

1000 − 700 = `___`

900 − 500 = `___`

800 − 300 = `___`

Change the order and add on.

A

7 + 8 = ⬜8⬜ + ⬜7⬜ = ⬜15⬜   4 + 16 = ⬜   10 + 27 = ⬜

9 + 11 = ⬜11⬜ + ⬜ = ⬜   8 + 9 = ⬜   10 + 45 = ⬜

5 + 7 = ⬜ + ⬜ = ⬜   6 + 5 = ⬜   10 + 39 = ⬜

3 + 13 = ⬜ + ⬜ = ⬜   2 + 14 = ⬜   10 + 82 = ⬜

6 + 9 = ⬜ + ⬜ = ⬜   5 + 8 = ⬜   10 + 68 = ⬜

B

8 + 37 = ⬜37⬜ + ⬜ = ⬜   9 + 56 = ⬜   30 + 70 = ⬜

6 + 64 = ⬜ + ⬜ = ⬜   3 + 79 = ⬜   20 + 50 = ⬜

9 + 78 = ⬜ + ⬜ = ⬜   5 + 46 = ⬜   40 + 60 = ⬜

5 + 49 = ⬜ + ⬜ = ⬜   8 + 35 = ⬜   20 + 30 = ⬜

7 + 85 = ⬜ + ⬜ = ⬜   6 + 67 = ⬜   30 + 40 = ⬜

4 + 28 = ⬜ + ⬜ = ⬜   7 + 29 = ⬜   40 + 50 = ⬜

C

6 + 328 = ⬜   9 + 607 = ⬜   80 + 470 = ⬜

9 + 745 = ⬜   7 + 276 = ⬜   60 + 650 = ⬜

4 + 587 = ⬜   3 + 438 = ⬜   20 + 290 = ⬜

8 + 339 = ⬜   8 + 127 = ⬜   70 + 760 = ⬜

5 + 168 = ⬜   6 + 856 = ⬜   40 + 380 = ⬜

7 + 913 = ⬜   5 + 397 = ⬜   90 + 540 = ⬜

Fill in the boxes.

A

3 + 3 + 4   10   2 + 3 + 2   ☐   3 + 4 + 1   ☐

5 + 4 + 2   ☐   2 + 4 + 3   ☐   1 + 5 + 3   ☐

2 + 5 + 5   ☐   3 + 5 + 4   ☐   4 + 3 + 5   ☐

4 + 5 + 1   ☐   1 + 4 + 5   ☐   5 + 1 + 5   ☐

4 + 4 + 4   ☐   5 + 3 + 3   ☐   4 + 4 + 2   ☐

B

Start with the largest number.

8 + 5 + 6   ☐   7 + 8 + 4   ☐   6 + 5 + 6   ☐

9 + 2 + 7   ☐   5 + 7 + 6   ☐   4 + 9 + 7   ☐

5 + 3 + 8   ☐   9 + 6 + 8   ☐   7 + 6 + 3   ☐

6 + 9 + 5   ☐   3 + 7 + 6   ☐   8 + 4 + 5   ☐

4 + 7 + 3   ☐   8 + 9 + 4   ☐   9 + 7 + 7   ☐

C

Start with the largest number.

5 + 13 + 7   ☐   9 + 2 + 17   ☐   6 + 6 + 16   ☐

9 + 4 + 16   ☐   4 + 8 + 15   ☐   7 + 14 + 2   ☐

3 + 6 + 11   ☐   6 + 19 + 5   ☐   3 + 11 + 8   ☐

7 + 18 + 6   ☐   3 + 12 + 7   ☐   6 + 4 + 17   ☐

5 + 14 + 8   ☐   9 + 4 + 13   ☐   5 + 9 + 15   ☐

Look at the pictograms. Fill in the boxes.

A

Favourite Drinks						
Apple	🥤	🥤	🥤	🥤		
Cola	🥤	🥤	🥤	🥤	🥤	
Milk	🥤	🥤				
Orange	🥤	🥤	🥤			
Water	🥤					

Votes	Drink
1	
2	
3	
4	
5	

B

People on a train					
Coach 1	🚂	🚂	🚂	🚂	🚂
Coach 2	🚂	🚂			
Coach 3	🚂	🚂	🚂	🚂	
Coach 4	🚂	🚂	🚂		

🚂 represents 5 people

How many more people on:

Coach 1 than Coach 2 ☐

Coach 3 than Coach 4? ☐

How many people altogether:

on Coach 1 and Coach 2 ☐

on the train? ☐

C

Pages read				
Thursday	📖	📖	📖	
Friday	📖	📖	📖	📖
Saturday	📖	📖		
Sunday	📖	📖	📖	📖	📖

 represents 10 pages

How many fewer pages read on:

Thursday than Friday ☐

Saturday than Sunday? ☐

How many pages read altogether:

on Saturday and Sunday ☐

in all 4 days? ☐

Finish the pictograms.

 A

Ages of girls at a party.

Age	Girls
5	2
6	5
7	6
8	4

Five	☺	☺				
Six						
Seven						
Eight						

 B

Number of throws hitting a target skittle in a PE lesson.

Thrower	Hits
Delon	8
Fred	10
Izzy	6
Sue	12

Delon						
Fred						
Izzy						
Sue						

 represents 2 hits

 C

Ice cream flavours sold in a shop.

Flavour	Sales
Chocolate	30
Mint	15
Strawberry	20
Vanilla	10

Chocolate						
Mint						
Strawberry						
Vanilla						

 represents 5 sales

A

Colour the 10 times table.

5	10	15	20	25	30	35	40	45	50	55	60
65	70	75	80	85	90	95	100	105	110	115	120

10 Times Table | 10 | 20 | | | | | | | | | | |

B

4 × 10 | 40 | 11 × 10 | | 90 ÷ 10 | | 110 ÷ 10 | |

10 × 10 | | 8 × 10 | | 60 ÷ 10 | | 20 ÷ 10 | |

2 × 10 | | 3 × 10 | | 100 ÷ 10 | | 50 ÷ 10 | |

7 × 10 | | 9 × 10 | | 10 ÷ 10 | | 120 ÷ 10 | |

12 × 10 | | 1 × 10 | | 70 ÷ 10 | | 30 ÷ 10 | |

5 × 10 | | 6 × 10 | | 40 ÷ 10 | | 80 ÷ 10 | |

C

| 5 | × 10 = 50 | | × 10 = 70 | | ÷ 10 = 6 | | ÷ 10 = 1 |

| | × 10 = 90 | | × 10 = 40 | | ÷ 10 = 2 | | ÷ 10 = 5 |

| | × 10 = 110 | | × 10 = 100 | | ÷ 10 = 10 | | ÷ 10 = 9 |

| | × 10 = 30 | | × 10 = 80 | | ÷ 10 = 7 | | ÷ 10 = 4 |

| | × 10 = 60 | | × 10 = 20 | | ÷ 10 = 12 | | ÷ 10 = 8 |

| | × 10 = 10 | | × 10 = 120 | | ÷ 10 = 3 | | ÷ 10 = 11 |

Write the times on the boxes.

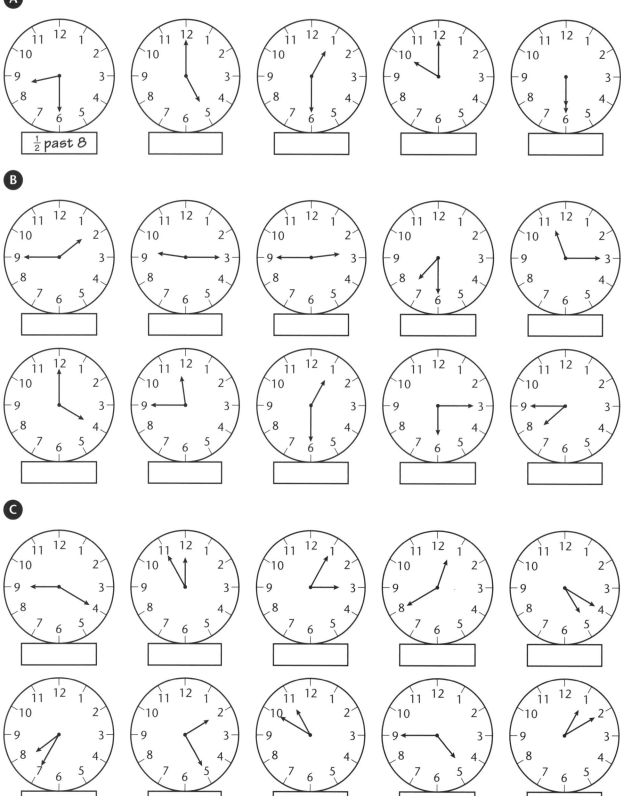

A

$\frac{1}{2}$ *past 8*

Fill in the boxes.

A

[ ] minutes in one hour.

[ ] hours in one day.

The minute hand takes [ ] minutes to go around the clock.

The hour hand takes [ ] hours to go once around the clock.

The minute hand takes [ ] minutes to go halfway round the clock.

The hour hand takes [ ] hours to go halfway round the clock.

B

How many minutes are left in the hour if the time is:

quarter to [ ]

20 past [ ]

quarter past [ ]

half past [ ]

5 past [ ]

How many hours is it until 12 o'clock if the time is:

4 o'clock [ ]

9 o'clock [ ]

1 o'clock [ ]

7 o'clock [ ]

11 o'clock [ ]

C

How many minutes are left in the hour if the time is:

3:27 [ ]   11:48 [ ]

7:04 [ ]   4:23 [ ]

1:52 [ ]   8:31 [ ]

10:19 [ ]   5:07 [ ]

6:35 [ ]   2:56 [ ]

How many hours are left in the day if the time is:

6:00 pm [ ]   4:00 pm [ ]

10:00 am [ ]   5:00 am [ ]

2:00 pm [ ]   11:00 pm [ ]

3:00 am [ ]   Noon [ ]

8:00 am [ ]   1:00 am [ ]

A

Write in figures.

fifteen	15
seventeen	
twelve	
eighteen	
fourteen	
twenty	
eleven	
sixteen	
thirteen	
nineteen	

Write as words.

12 ....twelve......

16 ....

19 ....

17 ....

13 ....

20 ....

11 ....

14 ....

B

Write in figures.

thirty-seven	
eighty	
sixty-two	
ninety-six	
twenty-four	
fifty-nine	
seventy-one	
forty-three	
one hundred	
eighty-seven	

Write as words.

65 ....

28 ....

93 ....

52 ....

74 ....

47 ....

89 ....

35 ....

C

Write in words.

625   six hundred and .... twenty-five ....

153 ....
....

830 ....
....

376 ....
....

598 ....
....

919 ....
....

467 ....
....

842 ....
....

201 ....
....

784 ....
....

539 ....
....

311 ....
....

Write the numbers in order, starting with the smallest.

A

| 9 | 4 | 15 | 7 | 11 |

| 4 | 7 | | | |

| 13 | 8 | 17 | 5 | 10 |

| | | | | |

| 12 | 21 | 9 | 16 | 19 |

| | | | | |

| 20 | 18 | 14 | 25 | 11 |

| | | | | |

| 31 | 13 | 22 | 28 | 16 |

| | | | | |

B

| 62 | 60 | 66 | 26 | 22 |

| | | | | |

| 39 | 30 | 93 | 90 | 33 |

| | | | | |

| 45 | 54 | 44 | 55 | 50 |

| | | | | |

| 77 | 70 | 17 | 7 | 71 |

| | | | | |

| 58 | 25 | 52 | 82 | 28 |

| | | | | |

C

| 173 | 317 | 177 | 337 | 137 |

| | | | | |

| 299 | 492 | 249 | 294 | 429 |

| | | | | |

| 858 | 586 | 888 | 568 | 885 |

| | | | | |

| 330 | 203 | 323 | 232 | 230 |

| | | | | |

| 574 | 547 | 475 | 745 | 457 |

| | | | | |

Fill in the boxes.

A

13 + 7	20	15 + 3		12 + 4		14 + 6	
11 + 8		12 + 5		14 + 3		17 + 2	
14 + 2		13 + 4		16 + 2		11 + 7	
16 + 4		11 + 6		11 + 5		13 + 2	
12 + 7		18 + 2		13 + 6		12 + 6	

B

36 + 5		47 + 9		58 + 9		85 + 6	
29 + 7		34 + 7		27 + 6		46 + 7	
55 + 8		69 + 6		72 + 9		38 + 6	
67 + 4		28 + 3		86 + 4		54 + 9	
43 + 9		75 + 9		64 + 8		89 + 8	
78 + 5		56 + 8		39 + 3		77 + 5	

C

435 + 9		259 + 5		126 + 8		397 + 6	
749 + 2		584 + 7		557 + 9		703 + 9	
187 + 5		196 + 9		365 + 7		668 + 5	
593 + 8		737 + 8		918 + 9		579 + 9	
276 + 6		348 + 4		799 + 4		145 + 8	
608 + 7		462 + 9		474 + 8		966 + 5	

Fill in the boxes.

A

7 and 6 make [ ] altogether.

Add 4 to 9. [ ]

Find the total of 14 and 6. [ ]

6 is 5 more than [ ].

Add together 8 and 8. [ ]

The sum of 10 and 4 is [ ].

5   plus   7   [ ]

8   plus   3   [ ]

7   plus   9   [ ]

12   plus   5   [ ]

4   plus   12   [ ]

9   plus   11   [ ]

B

9 greater than 28 is [ ].

Together 59 and 40 make [ ].

Find the sum of 53 and 12. [ ]

65 and 7 equals [ ].

34 plus 20 is [ ].

[ ] is 17 more than 41.

Find three one-digit numbers with these totals.

20	7	[ ]	[ ]
26	[ ]	[ ]	[ ]
23	[ ]	8	[ ]

C

54 is [ ] plus 8.

The total of 32 and [ ] is 92.

[ ] and 27 make 62 altogether.

[ ] more than 77 is 83.

[ ] equals 30 and 28.

46 is [ ] added to 84.

Find three two-digit numbers which give each total.

42	18	[ ]	[ ]
85	[ ]	29	[ ]
73	[ ]	[ ]	35

Examples

```
    4 7              4 7                 8 7
  + 3 2            + 3 9            +    3 9        7 + 9 = 16
  ......9  Add units  1 6           1 2 6          6 in units
    7 0  Add tens    7 0               1            Carry 10 (¹)
    7 9  Find total   8 6
```

Use the above examples. Set out in columns and work out.

A

```
    2 5        5 7
  + 2 1      + 3 2
  ....6........  ..........
    4 0
  _____        _____
```

```
    4 3        4 1
  + 1 4      + 2 4
  ..........  ..........
  _____        _____
  _____        _____
```

```
    3 2        5 4
  + 1 5      + 2 3
  ..........  ..........
  _____        _____
  _____        _____
```

```
    3 4        3 6
  + 2 0      + 3 2
  ..........  ..........
  _____        _____
  _____        _____
```

B

```
    3 6        3 7
  + 2 7      + 3 4
  ..........  ..........
  _____        _____
  _____        _____
```

```
    4 4        5 2
  + 2 8      + 2 6
  ..........  ..........
  _____        _____
  _____        _____
```

```
    5 7        4 9
  + 1 9      + 1 8
  ..........  ..........
  _____        _____
  _____        _____
```

```
    6 8        5 5
  + 2 5      + 3 6
  ..........  ..........
  _____        _____
  _____        _____
```

C

```
    5 9        9 0
  + 4 4      + 7 3
  _____        _____

    7 8        8 7
  + 6 3      + 7 5
  _____        _____

    8 6        6 9
  + 4 6      + 6 4
  _____        _____

    9 2        7 6
  + 5 7      + 3 5
  _____        _____

    6 7        5 8
  + 4 8      + 5 4
  _____        _____

    7 4        9 5
  + 2 7      + 6 9
  _____        _____
```

Write g or kg in the box.

table	kg	pillow		shoe	
goldfish		chicken		bed	
dog		bicycle		potato	
balloon		football		sheep	

Write 10 g, 100 g or 1 kg in the box.

a rubber	10 g	bag of sugar		oxo cube	
apple		toothpaste tube		chocolate bar	
brick		sweet		laptop computer	
coin		ice cream cone		cornflakes box	
plate		encyclopaedia		pen	

Fill in the box.

1 kg = [ ] g + 200 g   1 kg = [ ] g + 0 g

1 kg = [ ] g + 600 g   1 kg = [ ] g + 800 g

1 kg = [ ] g + 900 g   1 kg = [ ] g + 400 g

1 kg = [ ] g + 500 g   1 kg = [ ] g + 700 g

1 kg = [ ] g + 300 g   1 kg = [ ] g + 100 g

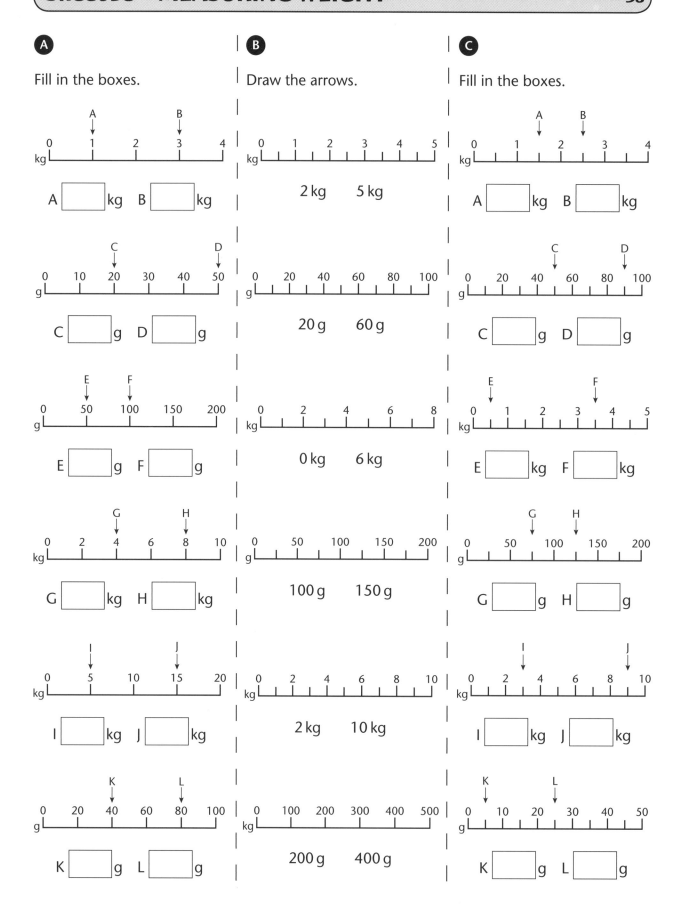

A

Fill in the boxes.

A [   ] kg B [   ] kg

C [   ] g D [   ] g

E [   ] g F [   ] g

G [   ] kg H [   ] kg

I [   ] kg J [   ] kg

K [   ] g L [   ] g

B

Draw the arrows.

2 kg   5 kg

20 g   60 g

0 kg   6 kg

100 g   150 g

2 kg   10 kg

200 g   400 g

C

Fill in the boxes.

A [   ] kg B [   ] kg

C [   ] g D [   ] g

E [   ] kg F [   ] kg

G [   ] g H [   ] g

I [   ] kg J [   ] kg

K [   ] g L [   ] g

Fill in the boxes.

A

12 − 7	5	16 − 5		11 − 6		16 − 8	
15 − 9		13 − 9		13 − 8		14 − 5	
14 − 8		17 − 8		18 − 9		11 − 9	
11 − 5		14 − 9		12 − 5		17 − 4	
13 − 4		19 − 5		20 − 7		12 − 3	

B

45 − 8		24 − 5		41 − 3		73 − 7	
62 − 7		81 − 6		63 − 4		92 − 9	
56 − 9		48 − 7		76 − 8		47 − 4	
74 − 7		72 − 4		50 − 9		54 − 8	
30 − 5		95 − 9		99 − 6		38 − 9	
93 − 9		17 − 8		85 − 7		61 − 7	

C

375 − 6		764 − 7		313 − 8		462 − 8	
691 − 8		940 − 3		732 − 6		525 − 9	
514 − 9		382 − 9		897 − 9		619 − 5	
142 − 5		451 − 5		174 − 6		283 − 6	
236 − 7		638 − 9		400 − 8		901 − 9	
853 − 5		505 − 8		621 − 4		750 − 1	

Fill in the boxes.

A

14 take 6 equals ☐ .   12   minus   5   ☐

7 fewer than 11 is ☐ .   16   minus   7   ☐

8 is 15 subtract ☐ .   20   minus 12   ☐

4 taken away from 20 leaves ☐ .   17   minus   4   ☐

3 equals ☐ less than 13.   15   minus   6   ☐

Take 9 from 18 to leave ☐ .   19   minus 15   ☐

B

28 less than 6 equals ☐ .   The difference between:

Take 40 from 75 to leave ☐ .   60   and 78 is ☐

38 minus 15 is ☐ .   52   and   9 is ☐

☐ equals 45 subtract 7.   80   and 16 is ☐

☐ is 20 fewer than 99.   30   and 83 is ☐

74 take away 17 is ☐ .   71   and   5 is ☐

C

Subtract 17 from 95 to leave ☐ .   The difference between:

470 is 200 fewer than ☐ .   41 and 25 is ☐

63 take 28 equals ☐ .   100 and 64 is ☐

☐ equals 509 minus 60.   74 and 26 is ☐

☐ equals 23 less than 50.   225 and 90 is ☐

186 take away 70 leaves ☐ .   66 and 39 is ☐

Examples

```
    7 9                    7 9             ⁶7¹2   2 − 4
  − 3 4                  − 3 4           − 3 4   Borrow 10 from 70 (⁶7¹2)
  ───────                ───────         ───────
      5   (9 − 4)          4 5             3 8   12 − 4 = 8
  ─────────              ───────                 60 − 30 = 30
    4 0   (70 − 30)
  ───────
    4 5   (5 + 40)
  ───────
```

Use the above examples. Set out in columns and work out.

Ⓐ

```
    4 8            3 4
  − 1 3          − 1 2
  ───────        ───────
      5          ...........
  .........        − −
    3 0          ───────
  ───────
  ───────


    3 6            2 7
  − 2 4          − 1 6
  ───────        ───────
  .........      .........
  ───────        ───────
  ───────        ───────


    2 9            4 5
  − 1 5          − 3 2
  ───────        ───────
  .........      .........
  ───────        ───────
  ───────        ───────


    5 5            5 7
  − 3 0          − 2 3
  ───────        ───────
  .........      .........
  ───────        ───────
  ───────        ───────
```

Ⓑ

```
    3 8            8 9
  − 1 5          − 3 6
  ───────        ───────


    4 9            7 5
  − 2 7          − 3 3
  ───────        ───────


    6 7            6 8
  − 2 5          − 4 2
  ───────        ───────


    9 4            8 6
  − 7 1          − 6 3
  ───────        ───────


    5 9            9 9
  − 3 4          − 3 8
  ───────        ───────


    7 8            7 7
  − 4 7          − 6 1
  ───────        ───────
```

Ⓒ

```
    8 2            7 1
  − 4 7          − 5 2
  ───────        ───────


    5 8            9 6
  − 2 6          − 2 7
  ───────        ───────


    7 3            8 4
  − 2 5          − 5 9
  ───────        ───────


    8 5            6 3
  − 1 9          − 5 8
  ───────        ───────


    9 0            5 2
  − 6 3          − 3 4
  ───────        ───────


    6 6            7 5
  − 3 6          − 4 6
  ───────        ───────
```

Make these amounts. Use the number of coins shown.

16p (10p) (5p) (1p)   65p ◯ ◯ ◯

72p ◯ ◯ ◯   14p ◯ ◯ ◯

45p ◯ ◯ ◯   31p ◯ ◯ ◯

B

Make the amounts shown in 2 different ways. Use 3 or 4 coins only.

◯ ◯ ◯ ◯   ◯ ◯ ◯ ◯

56p

◯ ◯ ◯ ◯   ◯ ◯ ◯ ◯   £3·50

◯ ◯ ◯ ◯   ◯ ◯ ◯ ◯

80p

◯ ◯ ◯ ◯   ◯ ◯ ◯ ◯   £1·30

Use no more than 5 coins. Make the amounts shown in 2 different ways.

95p   <u> 50p   20p   20p   5p </u>   74p   ....

95p   ....   74p   ....

£4·60   ....   £2·17   ....

£4·60   ....   £2·17   ....

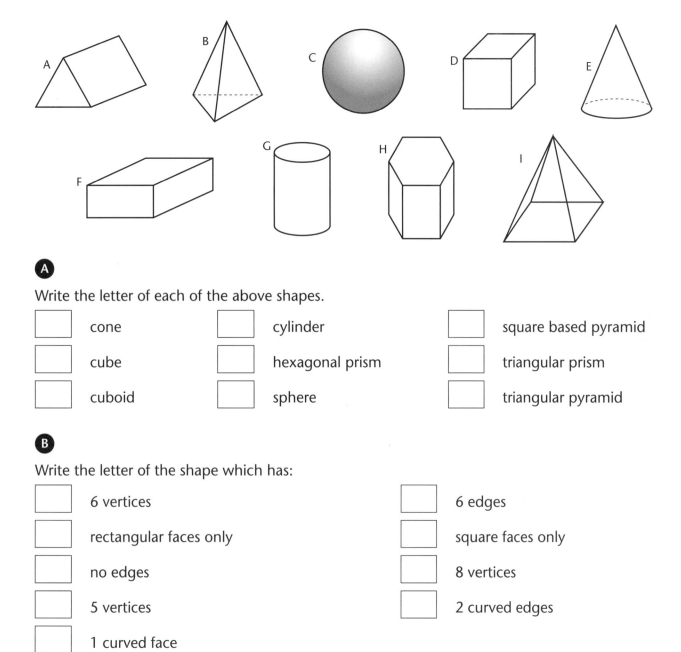

A

Write the letter of each of the above shapes.

	cone			cylinder			square based pyramid
	cube			hexagonal prism			triangular prism
	cuboid			sphere			triangular pyramid

B

Write the letter of the shape which has:

	6 vertices			6 edges
	rectangular faces only			square faces only
	no edges			8 vertices
	5 vertices			2 curved edges
	1 curved face			

C

Complete this table for the above shapes with straight edges.

	A	B	D	F	H	I
Faces	5					
Edges						
Vertices						

A

cone	cylinder
cube	prism
cuboid	pyramid

Use these words to name each shape.

triangular prism

....

square based

....

triangular

B

Write down all the 3-D shapes in A which have one or more faces which are:

CIRCULAR (2)

....

....

SQUARE (2)

....

....

....

RECTANGULAR (2)

....

....

....

TRIANGULAR (3)

....

....

....

CURVED (2)

....

....

C

Identify the 3-D shapes from its 2-D faces. Write the number of faces in the 2-D shapes.

1   4

square based pyramid
....

....

....

2
....

....

1
....

A

Colour in the odd one out.

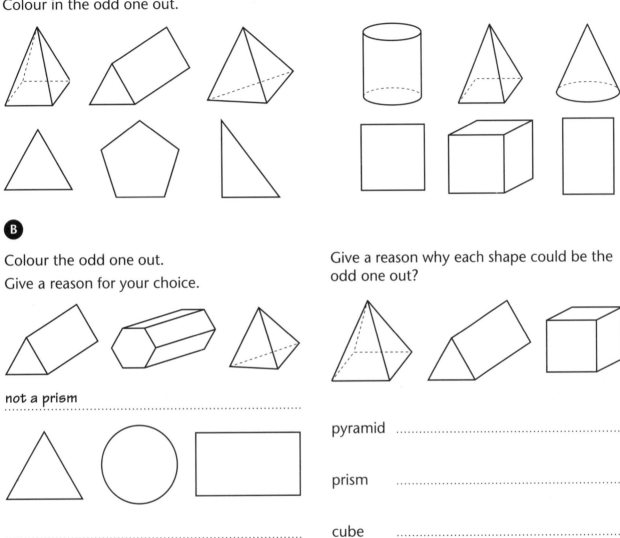

B

Colour the odd one out.
Give a reason for your choice.

Give a reason why each shape could be the odd one out?

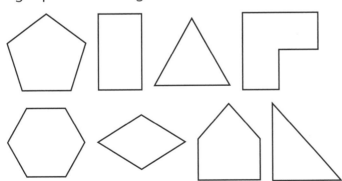

not a prism
....

pyramid ....

prism   ....

cube   ....

....

C

Sort the shapes by drawing them in the right part of the diagram.

	less than 5 sides	not less than 5 sides
all sides equal		
not all sides equal		

Fill in the estimate box (E).
Group the dots and count. Fill in the total box (T).

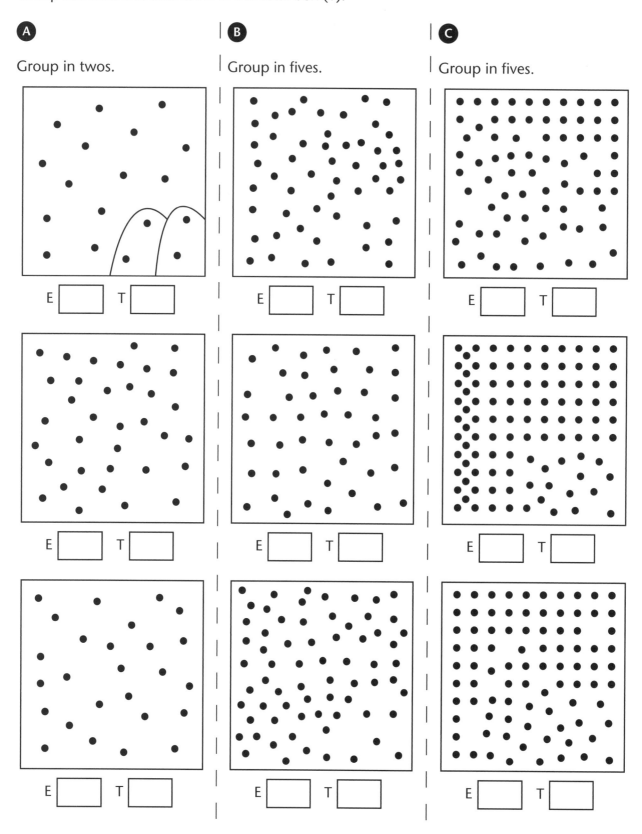

A

Group in twos.

E [   ]   T [   ]

E [   ]   T [   ]

E [   ]   T [   ]

B

Group in fives.

E [   ]   T [   ]

E [   ]   T [   ]

E [   ]   T [   ]

C

Group in fives.

E [   ]   T [   ]

E [   ]   T [   ]

E [   ]   T [   ]

A

Fill in the boxes.

0   5   10   ☐ ☐

25   30   35   ☐ ☐

40   45   50   ☐ ☐

15   20   25   ☐ ☐

30   35   40   ☐ ☐

Count on.

3 fives from 10   25

5 fives from 35   ☐

4 fives from 20   ☐

6 fives from 5   ☐

3 fives from 45   ☐

Count on.

7 fives from 0   ☐

5 fives from 30   ☐

6 fives from 15   ☐

3 fives from 45   ☐

5 fives from 25   ☐

B

Fill in the boxes.

45   50   55   ☐ ☐

35   30   25   ☐ ☐

80   85   90   ☐ ☐

60   55   50   ☐ ☐

55   60   65   ☐ ☐

Count on.

6 fives from 50   ☐

5 fives from 25   ☐

4 fives from 70   ☐

7 fives from 45   ☐

6 fives from 15   ☐

Count back.

5 fives from 65   ☐

3 fives from 70   ☐

4 fives from 45   ☐

6 fives from 100   ☐

5 fives from 85   ☐

C

Count on.

6 fives from 475   ☐

9 fives from 710   ☐

7 fives from 525   ☐

8 fives from 960   ☐

5 fives from 285   ☐

Count back.

5 fives from 920   ☐

8 fives from 115   ☐

4 fives from 400   ☐

6 fives from 845   ☐

9 fives from 770   ☐

How many 5s?

576 to 616   ☐

242 to 322   ☐

894 to 944   ☐

389 to 469   ☐

645 to 705   ☐

A

Colour the 5 times table.

1	2	3	4	5	6	7	8	9	10	11	12	13	14	15	16	17	18	19	20
21	22	23	24	25	26	27	28	29	30	31	32	33	34	35	36	37	38	39	40
41	42	43	44	45	46	47	48	49	50	51	52	53	54	55	56	57	58	59	60

5 Times Table   ..5....   ..10....   ....

B

6×5	30	8×5	☐	$15 \div 5$	☐	$45 \div 5$	☐
1×5	☐	10×5	☐	$35 \div 5$	☐	$30 \div 5$	☐
11×5	☐	2×5	☐	$50 \div 5$	☐	$20 \div 5$	☐
9×5	☐	7×5	☐	$25 \div 5$	☐	$60 \div 5$	☐
5×5	☐	3×5	☐	$5 \div 5$	☐	$40 \div 5$	☐
4×5	☐	12×5	☐	$55 \div 5$	☐	$10 \div 5$	☐

C

☐ $\times 5 = 20$	☐ $\times 5 = 35$	☐ $\div 5 = 5$	☐ $\div 5 = 10$
☐ $\times 5 = 30$	☐ $\times 5 = 10$	☐ $\div 5 = 9$	☐ $\div 5 = 6$
☐ $\times 5 = 5$	☐ $\times 5 = 50$	☐ $\div 5 = 3$	☐ $\div 5 = 12$
☐ $\times 5 = 40$	☐ $\times 5 = 25$	☐ $\div 5 = 11$	☐ $\div 5 = 1$
☐ $\times 5 = 60$	☐ $\times 5 = 45$	☐ $\div 5 = 2$	☐ $\div 5 = 4$
☐ $\times 5 = 15$	☐ $\times 5 = 55$	☐ $\div 5 = 8$	☐ $\div 5 = 7$

Move digits one space to the left to multiply.
Move digits one space to the right to divide.

A

$3 \times 10 =$ 30

$8 \times 10 =$

$5 \times 10 =$

$12 \times 10 =$

$100 \div 10 =$

$20 \div 10 =$

$90 \div 10 =$

$40 \div 10 =$

$11 \times 10 =$

$6 \times 10 =$

$10 \times 10 =$

$7 \times 10 =$

$10 \div 10 =$

$50 \div 10 =$

$80 \div 10 =$

$120 \div 10 =$

B

$60 \times 10 =$ 600

$90 \times 10 =$

$40 \times 10 =$

$100 \times 10 =$

$500 \div 10 =$

$1100 \div 10 =$

$700 \div 10 =$

$1200 \div 10 =$

$20 \times 10 =$

$80 \times 10 =$

$50 \times 10 =$

$30 \times 10 =$

$600 \div 10 =$

$1000 \div 10 =$

$400 \div 10 =$

$900 \div 10 =$

C

$15 \times 10 =$ 150

$43 \times 10 =$

$28 \times 10 =$

$94 \times 10 =$

$570 \div 10 =$

$390 \div 10 =$

$610 \div 10 =$

$760 \div 10 =$

$82 \times 10 =$

$24 \times 10 =$

$45 \times 10 =$

$98 \times 10 =$

$190 \div 10 =$

$530 \div 10 =$

$770 \div 10 =$

$310 \div 10 =$

Colour the fraction shown.

A | **B** | **C**

$\frac{1}{4}$

$\frac{1}{2}$

$\frac{1}{3}$

$\frac{2}{4}$

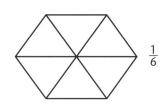

$\frac{1}{6}$

$\frac{2}{3}$

$\frac{1}{4}$

$\frac{1}{2}$

$\frac{1}{3}$

$\frac{1}{2}$

$\frac{3}{4}$

$\frac{1}{8}$

$\frac{1}{4}$

$\frac{1}{2}$

$\frac{1}{3}$

$\frac{1}{2}$

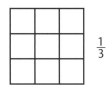

$\frac{1}{9}$

$\frac{1}{3}$

A

Colour the circles
half – red
quarter – blue

○ ○ ○ ○
○ ○ ○ ○

$\frac{1}{2}$ of 8 | 4 |

$\frac{1}{4}$ of 8 | |

○ ○ ○ ○
○ ○ ○ ○
○ ○ ○ ○
○ ○ ○ ○

$\frac{1}{2}$ of 16 | |

$\frac{1}{4}$ of 16 | |

○ ○ ○ ○ ○ ○
○ ○ ○ ○ ○ ○

$\frac{1}{2}$ of 12 | |

$\frac{1}{4}$ of 12 | |

○ ○ ○ ○ ○
○ ○ ○ ○ ○
○ ○ ○ ○ ○
○ ○ ○ ○ ○

$\frac{1}{2}$ of 20 | |

$\frac{1}{4}$ of 8 | |

B

Colour the squares
half – red
quarter – blue

□ □ □ □ □ □
□ □ □ □ □ □
□ □ □ □ □ □
□ □ □ □ □ □

$\frac{1}{2}$ of 24 | |

$\frac{1}{4}$ of 24 | |

□ □ □ □ □ □ □ □
□ □ □ □ □ □ □ □
□ □ □ □ □ □ □ □
□ □ □ □ □ □ □ □
□ □ □ □ □ □ □ □

$\frac{1}{2}$ of 40 | |

$\frac{1}{4}$ of 40 | |

Colour $\frac{1}{3}$ red.

□ □ □ □ □ □
□ □ □ □ □ □
□ □ □ □ □ □

$\frac{1}{3}$ of 18 | |

□ □ □ □ □ □ □ □ □
□ □ □ □ □ □ □ □ □
□ □ □ □ □ □ □ □ □
□ □ □ □ □ □ □ □ □

$\frac{1}{3}$ of 36 | |

C

Find one half of:

10 | |

18 | |

50 | |

80 | |

200 | |

Find one quarter of:

4 | |

24 | |

48 | |

100 | |

32 | |

Find one third of:

60 | |

33 | |

27 | |

300 | |

120 | |

Equivalent fractions are fractions that look different but are the same.

A

Shade the fraction shown.

 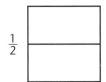  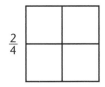

 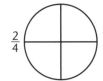  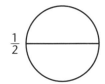

B

Colour the fractions to show that $\frac{1}{2} = \frac{2}{4}$.

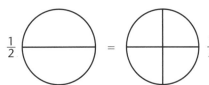 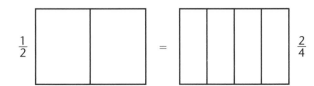

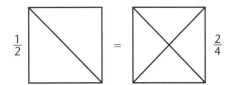 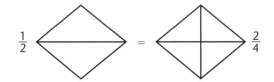

C

Colour each pair of fractions to show that they are equivalent.

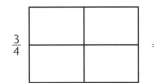 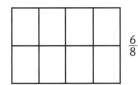 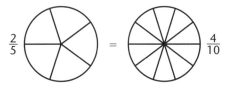

Fill in the boxes.

A

6 + 5   11

8 + 7   ☐

7 + 5   ☐

13 + 6   ☐

5 + 9   ☐

9 + 3   ☐

12 + 4   ☐

8 + 3   ☐

16 − 7   ☐

20 − 9   ☐

11 − 4   ☐

14 − 8   ☐

18 − 5   ☐

15 − 6   ☐

20 − 14   ☐

13 − 9   ☐

B

50 + 50   ☐

20 + 70   ☐

40 + 30   ☐

70 + 30   ☐

30 + 50   ☐

80 + 10   ☐

10 + 90   ☐

60 + 20   ☐

70 − 20   ☐

100 − 60   ☐

30 − 30   ☐

80 − 60   ☐

90 − 40   ☐

50 − 10   ☐

100 − 30   ☐

60 − 20   ☐

C

50 + 80   ☐

110 + 90   ☐

80 + 60   ☐

90 + 70   ☐

200 + 600   ☐

500 + 300   ☐

300 + 600   ☐

600 + 400   ☐

120 − 80   ☐

170 − 40   ☐

200 − 120   ☐

150 − 80   ☐

900 − 100   ☐

600 − 300   ☐

1000 − 500   ☐

800 − 600   ☐

Fill in the boxes.

A

$7 + 8 = 15$

$9 + \boxed{} = 13$

$\boxed{} + 6 = 11$

$8 + \boxed{} = 17$

$\boxed{} - 5 = 8$

$18 - \boxed{} = 12$

$\boxed{} - 7 = 9$

$20 - \boxed{} = 9$

$\boxed{} + 10 = 62$

$\boxed{} + 10 = 45$

$\boxed{} + 10 = 39$

$\boxed{} + 10 = 54$

$\boxed{} - 10 = 67$

$\boxed{} - 10 = 43$

$\boxed{} - 10 = 86$

$\boxed{} - 10 = 18$

B

$\boxed{} + 4 = 40$

$89 + \boxed{} = 96$

$\boxed{} + 8 = 72$

$27 + \boxed{} = 33$

$\boxed{} - 8 = 37$

$92 - \boxed{} = 86$

$\boxed{} - 7 = 63$

$54 - \boxed{} = 45$

$\boxed{} + 30 = 50$

$40 + \boxed{} = 90$

$\boxed{} + 20 = 89$

$34 + \boxed{} = 74$

$\boxed{} - 30 = 30$

$100 - \boxed{} = 40$

$\boxed{} - 20 = 73$

$87 - \boxed{} = 47$

C

$\boxed{} + 7 = 132$

$168 + \boxed{} = 171$

$\boxed{} + 9 = 258$

$576 + \boxed{} = 584$

$\boxed{} - 5 = 426$

$156 - \boxed{} = 148$

$\boxed{} - 9 = 794$

$372 - \boxed{} = 369$

$\boxed{} + 60 = 410$

$790 + \boxed{} = 830$

$\boxed{} + 80 = 508$

$151 + \boxed{} = 221$

$\boxed{} - 50 = 560$

$280 - \boxed{} = 190$

$\boxed{} - 60 = 831$

$558 - \boxed{} = 488$

Fill in the boxes.

A

6 red apples

8 green apples

[   ] apples altogether

16 white rolls

10 brown rolls

[   ] rolls altogether

Ali has 10p

Sam has 5p

They have [   ] p altogether

9 red flowers

7 blue flowers

[   ] flowers altogether

B

23 people downstairs

11 people upstairs

[   ] people on a bus

38 brown horses

5 white horses

[   ] horses altogether

46 litres of water in bath

30 litres of hot water added

[   ] litres of water in bath

Shane weighs 40 kg.

His dad weighs 25 kg more.

Shane's dad weighs [   ] kg.

C

57 cars in a car park

19 more came in

[   ] cars in the car park

35 apples are picked

92 apples left on tree

[   ] apples altogether

27 boys in Year 2

26 girls in Year 2

[   ] children in Year 2

320 fiction books

200 non-fiction books

[   ] books altogether.

Fill in the boxes.

A

12 sweets

3 are eaten

[ ] sweets left

16 balls in a box

11 are taken out

[ ] balls in the box

19 people on a bus

7 get off

[ ] people on the bus

28 children in a class

10 have a packed lunch

[ ] do not have a packed lunch

B

40 cards in a packet

30 are used

[ ] cards left

A drink costs 65p

Errol pays £1.

He is given [ ] p change

Dad is 33.

Mum is 4 year younger.

Mum is [ ].

Amy's book has 84 pages.

She has read 50.

She has [ ] pages left.

C

Barry has £81.

Larry has £38 less.

Larry has £ [ ]

A school has 311 pupils.

80 are on a trip to a museum.

There are [ ] pupils in school.

A bottle holds 1000 ml of milk.

300 ml is used.

[ ] ml is left.

245 seats in a cinema

7 are empty

[ ] seats are taken.

Look at the graphs. Fill in the boxes.

A

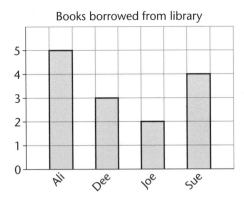

Books borrowed from library

Dee chose [ ] books.

[ ] chose 4 books.

[ ] chose most books.

[ ] chose fewest books.

[ ] books chosen altogether.

B

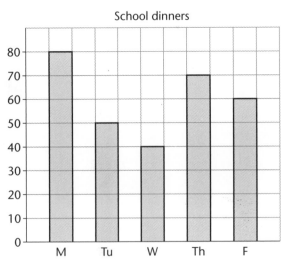

School dinners

The number of school dinners was:

[ ] on Wednesday

60 on [ ]

[ ] more on Monday than Tuesday

[ ] fewer on Wednesday than Thursday

[ ] on Monday and Tuesday altogether

[ ] in the whole week altogether.

C

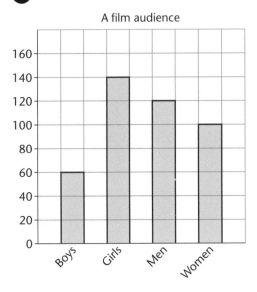

A film audience

[ ] fewer men than women

[ ] more boys than girls

[ ] adults

[ ] children

Total audience [ ]

Complete the graphs.

A

Favourite fruit

Fruit	Votes
Apples	2
Bananas	5
Grapes	3
Peaches	4

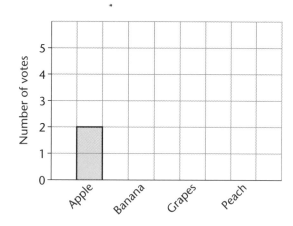

B

Favourite colours

Colour	Votes
Blue	20
Green	10
Red	25
Yellow	15

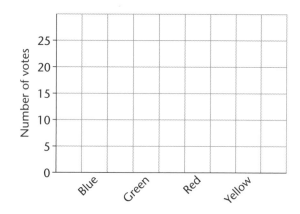

C

Plane passengers

Group	Number
Boys	40
Girls	60
Men	100
Women	80

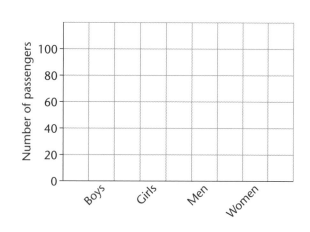

Write the missing numbers. Use the 3 given numbers only.

A

5 × 7 = ☐ 35

7 × 5 = ☐

35 ÷ 7 = ☐

35 ÷ 5 = ☐

4 × 5 = ☐

5 × 4 = ☐

20 ÷ 4 = ☐

20 ÷ 5 = ☐

9 × 2 = ☐

2 × 9 = ☐

18 ÷ 2 = ☐

18 ÷ 9 = ☐

6 × 10 = ☐

10 × 6 = ☐

60 ÷ 10 = ☐

60 ÷ 6 = ☐

B

12 × 5 = ☐

5 × ☐ = ☐

60 ÷ ☐ = ☐

60 ÷ ☐ = ☐

7 × 2 = ☐

2 × ☐ = ☐

☐ ÷ ☐ = ☐

☐ ÷ ☐ = ☐

8 × 10 = ☐

☐ × ☐ = ☐

☐ ÷ ☐ = ☐

☐ ÷ ☐ = ☐

4 × 3 = ☐

☐ × ☐ = ☐

☐ ÷ ☐ = ☐

☐ ÷ ☐ = ☐

C

3 × 6 = ☐

☐ × ☐ = ☐

☐ ÷ ☐ = ☐

☐ ÷ ☐ = ☐

7 × 4 = ☐

☐ × ☐ = ☐

☐ ÷ ☐ = ☐

☐ ÷ ☐ = ☐

24 ÷ 3 = ☐

☐ ÷ ☐ = ☐

☐ × ☐ = ☐

☐ × ☐ = ☐

99 ÷ 9 = ☐

☐ ÷ ☐ = ☐

☐ × ☐ = ☐

☐ × ☐ = ☐

Write the number sentence and work out.

 A

Multiply 4 by 5.

| 4 | × | 5 | = | |

Find 6 times 10.

| | | | = | |

What is double 8?

| | | | = | |

Find one half of 10.

| | | | = | |

Share 15 by 5.

| | | | = | |

Divide 40 by 10.

| | | | = | |

 B

Find 9 multiplied by 2.

| | | | = | |

Halve 100.

| | | | = | |

How many 5s make 60?

| | | | = | |

How many is 9 lots of 5?

| | | | = | |

What is 10 times larger than 10?

| | | | = | |

What is 10 divided by 10?

| | | | = | |

 C

50 fish. 10 tanks. How many in each? 50 ÷ 10 = ☐	35 sweets. 5 friends. How many each?	8 books in each pile. 5 piles. How many books? ....
25 girls. Equal boys and girls. How many children?	16 pencils in a box. 10 boxes. How many pencils?	60 children. 2 classes. How many in each? ....

Fill in the box.

A

5 bananas in each bunch.

3 bunches.

☐ bananas altogether.

2 bowls.

4 fish in each bowl.

☐ fish altogether.

10 sweets in a packet.

2 friends.

☐ sweets each.

9 cakes.

3 plates.

☐ cakes on each plate.

B

14 socks.

How many pairs?

Answer ☐ pairs.

6 eggs in each box.

10 boxes.

☐ eggs altogether.

12 pins in one packet.

How many pins in 2 packets?

Answer ☐ pins.

5 sweets cost 45p altogether.

How much does one sweet cost?

Answer ☐ p.

C

Two classes.

30 children in each.

☐ children altogether.

4 packets of fish fingers.

32 fish fingers altogether.

☐ fingers in each packet.

3 boxes hold 18 cakes altogether.

How many cakes in each box?

Answer ☐ cakes.

How much is five 20p coins?

Answer ☐ p.

Draw the hands on the clocks.

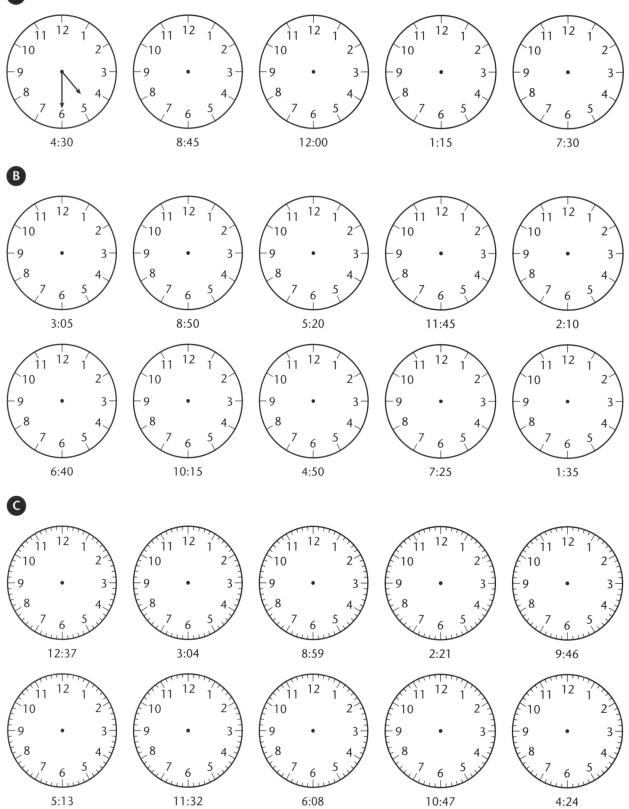

A

4:30   8:45   12:00   1:15   7:30

B

3:05   8:50   5:20   11:45   2:10

6:40   10:15   4:50   7:25   1:35

C

12:37   3:04   8:59   2:21   9:46

5:13   11:32   6:08   10:47   4:24

Write the day which comes:

after Tuesday .... before Tuesday ....

after Thursday .... before Monday ....

after Monday .... before Thursday ....

after Friday .... before Sunday ....

B

April	February	June	November
August	January	March	October
December	July	May	September

Write the months in the right order

1 January......................   5 ....   9 ....

2 ....   6 ....   10 ....

3 ....   7 ....   11 ....

4 ....   8 ....   12 ....

Look at the calendar.

July 1st is a ....

July 26th is a ....

July 17th is a ....

August 1st is a ....

There are .... Thursdays in July.

The third Saturday in July is the ....th.

JULY						
Su	M	Tu	W	Th	F	Sa
			1	2	3	4
5	6	7	8	9	10	11
12	13	14	15	16	17	18
19	20	21	22	23	24	25
26	27	28	29	30	31	

A

Fill in the boxes.

20 30 40 ☐ ☐

50 60 70 ☐ ☐

0 10 20 ☐ ☐

60 70 80 ☐ ☐

40 50 60 ☐ ☐

Count on.

5 tens from 30 | 80 |

4 tens from 10   ☐

3 tens from 70   ☐

6 tens from 0   ☐

5 tens from 20   ☐

Count on.

6 tens from 10   ☐

7 tens from 30   ☐

5 tens from 0   ☐

3 tens from 40   ☐

5 tens from 50   ☐

B

Fill in the boxes.

53 63 73 ☐ ☐

72 62 52 ☐ ☐

15 ☐ ☐ ☐ 55

108 ☐ ☐ ☐ 68

27 ☐ ☐ ☐ 67

Count on.

3 tens from 44   ☐

7 tens from 9   ☐

4 tens from 61   ☐

5 tens from 36   ☐

7 tens from 23   ☐

Count back.

6 tens from 95   ☐

4 tens from 48   ☐

5 tens from 102 ☐

4 tens from 87   ☐

7 tens from 76   ☐

C

Count on.

6 tens from 157   ☐

8 tens from 471   ☐

7 tens from 738   ☐

6 tens from 363   ☐

5 tens from 286   ☐

Count back.

8 tens from 935   ☐

4 tens from 509   ☐

9 tens from 872   ☐

8 tens from 414   ☐

7 tens from 657   ☐

How many 10s?

576 to 616   ☐

242 to 322   ☐

894 to 944   ☐

389 to 469   ☐

645 to 705   ☐

Fill in the boxes.

A

72 = 70 + ☐

16 = ☐ + 6

59 = 50 + ☐

85 = ☐ + 5

27 = 20 + ☐

95 = ☐ + 5

63 = 60 + ☐

41 = ☐ + 1

36 = 30 + ☐

78 = ☐ + 8

54 = 50 + ☐

29 = ☐ + 9

87 = 80 + ☐

13 = ☐ + 3

65 = 60 + ☐

B

48 = 30 + 18

96 = 80 + ☐

37 = ☐ + 17

75 = 60 + ☐

21 = ☐ + 11

84 = 70 + ☐

52 = ☐ + 12

67 = 50 + ☐

79 = ☐ + 19

45 = 30 + ☐

98 = ☐ + 18

26 = 10 + ☐

83 = ☐ + 13

35 = 20 + ☐

64 = ☐ + 14

C

317 = ☐ + 17

792 = 700 + ☐

564 = ☐ + 4

256 = 200 + ☐

631 = ☐ + 31

146 = 140 + ☐

889 = ☐ + 9

423 = 400 + ☐

974 = ☐ + 74

358 = 350 + ☐

568 = ☐ + 8

215 = 210 + ☐

739 = ☐ + 39

191 = 100 + ☐

642 = ☐ + 2

Fill in the boxes.

A

35 + 10   45

71 + 10

28 + 10

43 + 10

64 + 10

87 + 10

39 + 10

52 + 10

19 + 10

47 + 10

56 + 10

85 + 10

22 + 10

78 + 10

67 + 10

32 + 10

B

62 + 30

37 + 20

59 + 20

23 + 40

41 + 40

75 + 20

18 + 50

53 + 30

29 + 50

34 + 30

75 + 20

46 + 30

61 + 20

58 + 40

25 + 20

49 + 20

C

127 + 30

245 + 20

579 + 40

836 + 30

351 + 30

198 + 60

424 + 70

265 + 20

738 + 20

142 + 40

676 + 30

354 + 40

221 + 40

569 + 30

957 + 20

883 + 40

Fill in the boxes.

A

Start with the largest number or look for pairs that add up to 10.

7 + 4 + 6	17	4 + 3 + 7	
3 + 9 + 4		8 + 5 + 2	
5 + 2 + 8		1 + 9 + 6	
2 + 6 + 7		9 + 5 + 4	
6 + 9 + 3		5 + 7 + 2	

3 + 6 + 8 ☐
6 + 1 + 7 ☐
2 + 9 + 4 ☐
7 + 5 + 3 ☐
4 + 3 + 8 ☐

B

☐ + 4 + 9 = 21   6 + 4 + ☐ = 16   ☐ + 9 + 4 = 18

5 + ☐ + 5 = 17   8 + ☐ + 5 = 20   6 + ☐ + 7 = 20

9 + 6 + ☐ = 18   ☐ + 9 + 3 = 19   8 + 5 + ☐ = 19

7 + ☐ + 4 = 19   3 + ☐ + 8 = 17   7 + ☐ + 8 = 17

☐ + 9 + 8 = 21   9 + 5 + ☐ = 21   ☐ + 6 + 9 = 24

C

5 + 14 + ☐ = 27   ☐ + 5 + 13 = 27   2 + 6 + ☐ = 20

7 + ☐ + 11 = 22   6 + ☐ + 16 = 29   7 + ☐ + 19 = 31

☐ + 9 + 19 = 31   8 + 3 + ☐ = 26   ☐ + 11 + 7 = 27

6 + ☐ + 17 = 28   7 + ☐ + 7 = 32   8 + ☐ + 16 = 32

12 + 6 + ☐ = 26   ☐ + 8 + 14 = 31   6 + 9 + ☐ = 33

Fill in the boxes.

A

3 more than 10 is ☐.

8 add 6 equals ☐.

The total of 7 and 11 is ☐.

Altogether 9 and 5 make ☐.

How many is 7 added to 7? ☐

Add 5 and 13 to make ☐.

6	plus	9	☐
14	plus	3	☐
5	plus	8	☐
8	plus	12	☐
10	plus	0	☐
7	plus	5	☐

B

8 plus 47 equals ☐.

☐ is 30 added to 19.

Which number is 43 add 28? ☐

76 and 5 make ☐ altogether.

25 larger than 50 is ☐.

☐ is the sum of 55 and 39.

Find three one-digit numbers which total:

18	6	☐	☐
21	☐	5	☐
25	☐	☐	☐

C

46 is the total of 26 and ☐.

64 is 7 more than ☐.

☐ plus 29 makes 91.

Add 40 and ☐ to make 73.

The sum of ☐ and 9 is 90.

83 equals 46 plus ☐.

Find three two-digit numbers which total.

50	☐	☐	11
63	☐	17	☐
84	39	☐	☐

A

Write ml or l (litres) in the box.

pool	l	ice cream cone		washing up bowl	
cup		saucepan		water pistol	
bucket		can of drink		lake	
glass		oil drum		cereal bowl	

B

Colour the most sensible estimate.

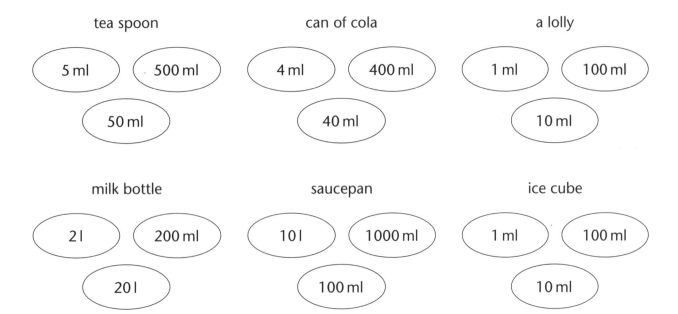

tea spoon

5 ml   500 ml
50 ml

can of cola

4 ml   400 ml
40 ml

a lolly

1 ml   100 ml
10 ml

milk bottle

2 l   200 ml
20 l

saucepan

10 l   1000 ml
100 ml

ice cube

1 ml   100 ml
10 ml

C

Fill in the box.

1 litre = ⬚ ml + 700 ml   1 litre = ⬚ ml + 500 ml

1 litre = ⬚ ml + 100 ml   1 litre = ⬚ ml + 300 ml

1 litre = ⬚ ml + 1000 ml   1 litre = ⬚ ml + 900 ml

1 litre = ⬚ ml + 400 ml   1 litre = ⬚ ml + 200 ml

1 litre = ⬚ ml + 800 ml   1 litre = ⬚ ml + 600 ml

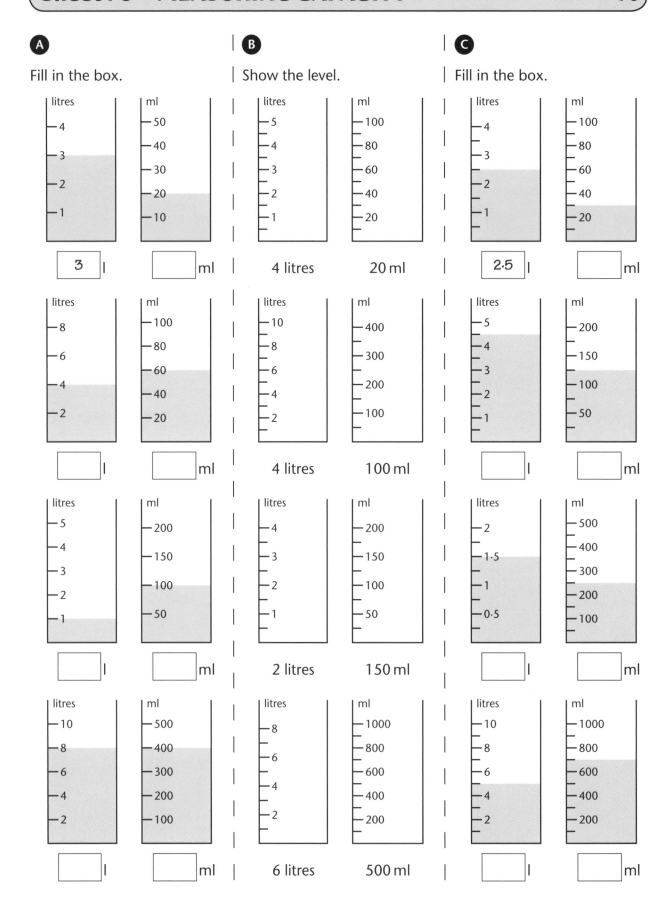

A

Fill in the box.

3 l

___ ml

___ l

___ ml

___ l

___ ml

___ l

___ ml

B

Show the level.

4 litres   20 ml

4 litres   100 ml

2 litres   150 ml

6 litres   500 ml

C

Fill in the box.

2·5 l

___ ml

___ l

___ ml

___ l

___ ml

___ l

___ ml

A

Fill in the box.

100 cm = [1] m

500 cm = [ ] m

800 cm = [ ] m

300 cm = [ ] m

2 m = [ ] cm

10 m = [ ] cm

4 m = [ ] cm

7 m = [ ] cm

1000 ml = [ ] litre

4000 ml = [ ] litres

2 litres = [ ] ml

5 litres = [ ] ml

1000 g = [ ] kg

3000 g = [ ] kg

5 kg = [ ] g

2 kg = [ ] g

B

Write >, < or =.

70 cm [>] 17 cm

200 cm [ ] 2 m

600 cm [ ] 66 m

90 cm [ ] 9 m

3 m [ ] 300 cm

5 m [ ] 50 cm

1 m [ ] 110 cm

6 m [ ] 600 cm

3 litres [ ] 3000 ml

7 litres [ ] 700 ml

6 litres [ ] 6000 ml

1 litre [ ] 10 000 ml

400 g [ ] 4 kg

8000 g [ ] 8 kg

300 g [ ] 3 kg

9000 g [ ] 9 kg

C

Fill in the box.

50 mm = [ ] cm

20 mm = [ ] cm

10 cm = [ ] mm

4 cm = [ ] mm

2000 m = [ ] km

8000 m = [ ] km

1 km = [ ] m

3 km = [ ] m

Make 1 litre

400 ml + [ ] ml

900 ml + [ ] ml

250 ml + [ ] ml

50 ml + [ ] ml

Make 1 kilogram

700 g + [ ] g

200 g + [ ] g

450 g + [ ] g

850 g + [ ] g

Fill in the boxes.

A

63 − 10 [53]

48 − 10 [ ]

97 − 10 [ ]

25 − 10 [ ]

71 − 10 [ ]

39 − 10 [ ]

54 − 10 [ ]

83 − 10 [ ]

42 − 10 [ ]

95 − 10 [ ]

29 − 10 [ ]

67 − 10 [ ]

58 − 10 [ ]

82 − 10 [ ]

34 − 10 [ ]

76 − 10 [ ]

B

73 − 20 [ ]

26 − 10 [ ]

51 − 40 [ ]

65 − 30 [ ]

87 − 20 [ ]

38 − 30 [ ]

93 − 60 [ ]

49 − 20 [ ]

57 − 30 [ ]

24 − 20 [ ]

78 − 40 [ ]

32 − 20 [ ]

41 − 40 [ ]

96 − 20 [ ]

69 − 50 [ ]

85 − 60 [ ]

C

346 − 30 [ ]

172 − 60 [ ]

517 − 20 [ ]

255 − 50 [ ]

123 − 40 [ ]

689 − 70 [ ]

905 − 50 [ ]

798 − 40 [ ]

236 − 50 [ ]

464 − 20 [ ]

812 − 40 [ ]

559 − 90 [ ]

181 − 30 [ ]

345 − 70 [ ]

703 − 20 [ ]

677 − 50 [ ]

Fill in the boxes.

A

8 less than 16 equals ☐.

Subtract 13 from 20 to leave ☐.

13 take 7 is ☐.

9 is ☐ fewer than 17.

12 subtract 9 equals ☐.

14 taken away from 19 is ☐.

18   minus   6   ☐

11   minus   3   ☐

15   minus   5   ☐

20   minus   11   ☐

14   minus   9   ☐

17   minus   6   ☐

B

Take 50 away from 66 to leave ☐.

88 subtract 27 is ☐.

☐ is 8 less than 31.

78 equals ☐ minus 40.

62 take 14 equals ☐.

7 fewer than 94 is ☐.

The difference between:

75   and   16   is   ☐

27   and   9   is   ☐

30   and   54   is   ☐

69   and   24   is   ☐

55   and   6   is   ☐

C

80 minus 37 equals ☐.

Take 47 from 82 to leave ☐.

20 less than 112 is ☐.

71 subtract 55 leaves ☐.

☐ is 80 fewer than 750.

29 taken away from 100 is ☐.

The difference between:

92   and   64   is   ☐

820   and   300   is   ☐

95   and   28   is   ☐

500   and   40   is   ☐

72   and   36   is   ☐

Fill in the box.

A

7 chocolate biscuits

5 plain biscuits

[ ] biscuits altogether

Cindy has 18p.

She spends 15p.

She has [ ] p left.

The classroom is 10 m long.

The Hall is 14 m longer.

The Hall is [ ] m long

20 pins in a box

6 are used

[ ] pins left

B

A drink costs 35p.

A cake costs 50p.

Together they cost [ ] p.

60 children in Year 2

4 are away

[ ] childen in school

English lasts 55 minutes.

Music is 20 minutes shorter.

Music lasts [ ] minutes

Karen is on page 43.

She reads 8 more pages.

She is on page [ ].

C

100 tissues in a box

35 are used

[ ] tissues left

120 sheep in one field

60 sheep in the next field

[ ] sheep altogether

65 adults

17 children

[ ] people

119 children in a school

90 have a school dinner

[ ] do not have a school dinner.

Write the missing number in the box.

A

Make 10p

| 10 | × 1p |

[ ] × 2p

[ ] × 5p

[ ] × 10p

Make 20p

[ ] × 1p

[ ] × 2p

[ ] × 5p

[ ] × 10p

Make 50p

[ ] × 2p

[ ] × 5p

[ ] × 10p

[ ] × 50p

Make £1

[ ] × 1p

[ ] × 10p

[ ] × 20p

[ ] × 50p

B

Make £1

[ ] × 1p

[ ] × 2p

[ ] × 5p

[ ] × 10p

[ ] × 20p

Make £2

[ ] × £1

[ ] × 50p

[ ] × 20p

[ ] × 10p

[ ] × 5p

Make £5

[ ] × £1

[ ] × 50p

[ ] × 20p

[ ] × 10p

[ ] × 5p

Make £10

[ ] × £5

[ ] × £2

[ ] × £1

[ ] × 50p

[ ] × 10p

C

Make £10

[ ] × 20p

[ ] × 10p

[ ] × 5p

[ ] × 2p

[ ] × 1p

Make £50

[ ] × £10

[ ] × £5

[ ] × £2

[ ] × 50p

[ ] × 10p

Make £100

[ ] × £20

[ ] × £10

[ ] × £5

[ ] × £2

[ ] × 50p

Make £200

[ ] × £20

[ ] × £10

[ ] × £5

[ ] × £2

[ ] × 20p

Fill in the box.

A

One 50p coin.

One 20p coin.

[ ] p altogether.

Charlie has £9.

Asif has £4 more.

Asif has £ [ ] .

Cola costs 59p.

Orange costs 10p less.

Orange costs [ ] p.

Carly has 20p.

She spends 6p.

She now has [ ] p.

B

A small lolly costs 65p.

A large lolly costs 30p more.

A large lolly costs [ ] p.

Tommy has 58p.

He finds 5p.

He now has [ ] p.

Together a pencil and a rubber cost 65p.

The rubber costs 40p.

The pencil costs [ ] p.

Some sweets cost 30p.

I pay with 50p.

I am given [ ] p change.

C

A TV costs £399.

In a sale its price is £50 less.

It now costs £ [ ] .

I pay £1.

I am given 28p change.

I spent [ ] p.

Judy has 47p.

Jayne has 29p.

Together they have [ ] p.

A sandwich costs £2·45.

A roll costs £1·65.

The sandwich costs [ ] p more.

A

D	E	F	G
C	N	O	H
B	M	P	I
A	L	K	J

Write the letter you find:

above N — E

below P — ☐

to the left of M — ☐

to the right of O — ☐

between N and L — ☐

2 squares below F — ☐

3 squares above A — ☐

in the bottom right hand corner — ☐

furthest away from A — ☐

between C and O — ☐

2 squares to the right of D — ☐

3 squares to the left of J — ☐

B

	P		
		O	

Write the letter in the given position:

A   above O

B   2 squares below P

C   in the top left hand corner

D   between P and A

E   to the right of C

F   2 squares above O

G   3 squares to the left of O

H   between P and B

I   in the bottom left hand corner

J   above D

K   below O

L   between H and O

M   on the bottom row

N   in the only place left

C

	A	B	C	D
4	●	△	⊠	◠
3	□	◆	⊖	▲
2	◈	⊗	◗	○
1	⌓	■	△	◇

Draw the shape found at:

B1 — ☐   D1 — ☐

D4 — ☐   A3 — ☐

A2 — ☐   C4 — ☐

C3 — ☐   B2 — ☐

B3 — ☐   D3 — ☐

D2 — ☐   A1 — ☐

A4 — ☐   C2 — ☐

C1 — ☐   B4 — ☐

Grid (columns 3, 4, 5 arrows at top; 6, 7 on right; 10, 9, 8 at bottom; 2, 1 on left):

		↓3	↓4			↓5	
M			A		Z	C	←6
E		N	F	R	S		Y	2→
L	X		K			J	D	←7
W		I		B	V	O	P	1→
	G		T	U		Q	H	

(↑10 ↑9 ↑8)

Examples

F2	=	Forward 2 squares
B3	=	Back 3 squares
QTR	=	Quarter turn to right
QTL	=	Quarter turn to left

A

Follow the directions.
Write the letter you find.

Start at 10
F3   QTR
F2   ☐

Start at 6
F4   QTL
F3   ☐

Start at 2
F7   QTR
F1   ☐

Start at 3
F5   QTL
F4   ☐

Start at 9
F3   QTR
F4   ☐

B

Follow the directions.
Write the letter you find.

Start at 7
F6   QTL
F1   QTR
F2   ☐

Start at 4
F4   QTL
B3   QTR
B1   ☐

Start at 10
F5   QTR
F4   QTL
B1   ☐

Start at 1
F3   QTL
F3   QTL
B3   ☐

C

Follow the directions.
Find the word.

Start at 8   F5   C
QTR   B3   ....
QTL   F4   ....

Start at 5   F4   ....
QTR   F5   ....
QTL   B2   ....
QTR   B2   ....

Write the directions.

Start at 2 .... F5 .... R
.... U
.... G
....

.... L
.... E
.... F
.... T

Draw the minute hand after making the turn shown.

A

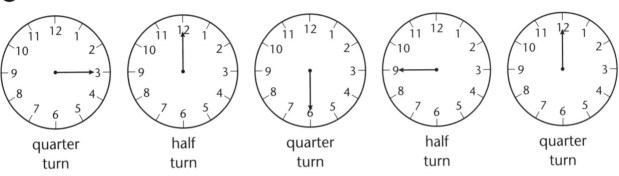

| quarter turn | half turn | quarter turn | half turn | quarter turn |

B

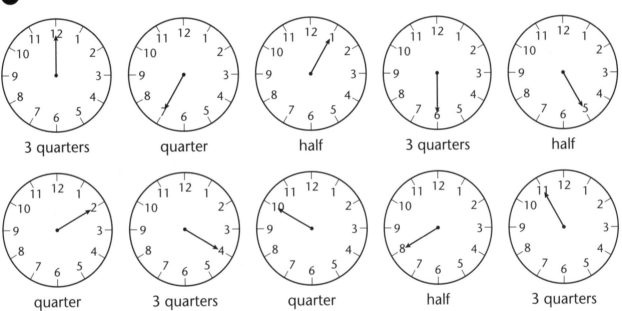

| 3 quarters | quarter | half | 3 quarters | half |

| quarter | 3 quarters | quarter | half | 3 quarters |

C

Write the new time if the hour hand makes these turns.

one quarter:	three quarters:	one half:	three quarters:
from 5 [8]	from 3 [ ]	from 4 [ ]	from 9 [ ]
from 1 [ ]	from 8 [ ]	from 11 [ ]	from 2 [ ]
from 11 [ ]	from 1 [ ]	from 2 [ ]	from 7 [ ]
from 4 [ ]	from 5 [ ]	from 7 [ ]	from 10 [ ]

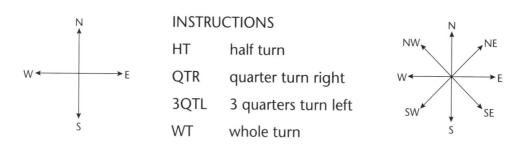

INSTRUCTIONS

HT   half turn

QTR   quarter turn right

3QTL   3 quarters turn left

WT   whole turn

Write down the direction you would be facing after making these turns.

A

Face North

HT | S |

QTL | W |

WT | |

Face West

HT | |

QTR | |

WT | |

Face South

HT | |

QTL | |

WT | |

Face East

HT | |

QTR | |

WT | |

B

Face North

3QTR | |

QTR | |

3QTL | |

Face South

3QTR | |

QTR | |

3QTL | |

Face West

3QTR | |

QTL | |

3QTL | |

Face East

3QTR | |

QTL | |

3QTL | |

C

Face NW

HT | |

QTL | |

3QTL | |

Face NE

QTR | |

3QTR | |

HT | |

Face SE

QTL | |

3QTL | |

QTR | |

Face SW

3QTR | |

QTL | |

3QTL | |

A

Fill in the boxes.

0	3	6	9	12

15	18	21	☐	27

9	12	15	18	☐

3	6	☐	12	15

24	27	30	☐	36

Start at 0. Count on.

4 threes   12

2 threes   ☐

5 threes   ☐

3 threes   ☐

6 threes   ☐

How many 3s?

6   2   threes

15   ☐   threes

9   ☐   threes

12   ☐   threes

30   ☐   threes

B

Fill in the boxes.

6	☐	12	15	☐

☐	24	27	☐	33

12	☐	18	21	☐

☐	21	24	☐	30

☐	27	30	33	☐

Start at 0. Count on.

7 threes   ☐

12 threes   ☐

8 threes   ☐

9 threes   ☐

11 threes   ☐

How many 3s?

18   ☐   threes

24   ☐   threes

15   ☐   threes

36   ☐   threes

27   ☐   threes

C

Write the missing number in the box.

6×3 18

11×3 ☐

9×3 ☐

$30 \div 3$ ☐

$24 \div 3$ ☐

$18 \div 3$ ☐

5×3 ☐

8×3 ☐

12×3 ☐

$21 \div 3$ ☐

$9 \div 3$ ☐

$33 \div 3$ ☐

10×3 ☐

4×3 ☐

7×3 ☐

$27 \div 3$ ☐

$15 \div 3$ ☐

$36 \div 3$ ☐

Write your estimate of each number shown in the box.

A

The answers are:

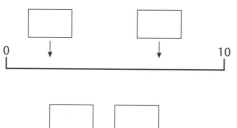

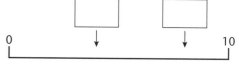

(1s)

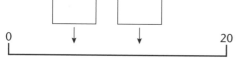

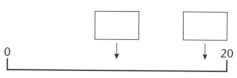

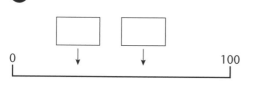

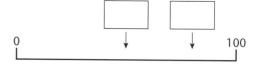

(2s)

B

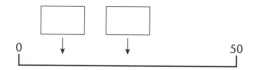

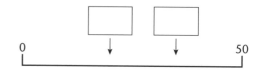

(10s)

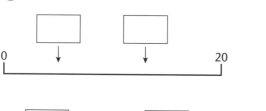

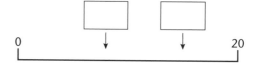

(5s)

C

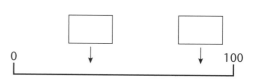

(1s)

(5s)

Write out each table.

TWOS   ..2.. ..4.. ..6.. ....

FIVES ....

TENS   ....

Fill in the boxes.

5 × 2 [10]	7 × 2 [ ]	22 ÷ 2 [ ]	12 ÷ 2 [ ]
4 × 5 [ ]	11 × 5 [ ]	10 ÷ 5 [ ]	60 ÷ 5 [ ]
11 × 10 [ ]	5 × 10 [ ]	30 ÷ 10 [ ]	70 ÷ 10 [ ]
12 × 2 [ ]	8 × 2 [ ]	18 ÷ 2 [ ]	20 ÷ 2 [ ]
9 × 5 [ ]	6 × 5 [ ]	35 ÷ 5 [ ]	40 ÷ 5 [ ]
6 × 10 [ ]	10 × 10 [ ]	120 ÷ 10 [ ]	90 ÷ 10 [ ]

C

Fill in the boxes.

[8] × 2 = 16	[ ] × 2 = 22	[ ] ÷ 2 = 9	[ ] ÷ 2 = 10
[ ] × 5 =	[ ] × 5 = 5	[ ] ÷ 5 = 7	[ ] ÷ 5 = 8
[ ] × 10 =	[ ] × 10 = 100	[ ] ÷ 10 = 11	[ ] ÷ 10 = 10
[ ] × 2 =	[ ] × 2 = 12	[ ] ÷ 2 = 4	[ ] ÷ 2 = 5
[ ] × 5 =	[ ] × 5 = 60	[ ] ÷ 5 = 9	[ ] ÷ 5 = 6
[ ] × 10 =	[ ] × 10 = 90	[ ] ÷ 10 = 2	[ ] ÷ 10 = 3

Change the order and multiply.

A

2 × 6 =	6	×	2	=	12	

2 × 6 = [6] × [2] = [12]   10 × 7 = [ ] × [ ] = [ ]

5 × 3 = [ ] × [ ] = [ ]   2 × 4 = [ ] × [ ] = [ ]

10 × 4 = [ ] × [ ] = [ ]   5 × 6 = [ ] × [ ] = [ ]

2 × 11 = [ ] × [ ] = [ ]   10 × 8 = [ ] × [ ] = [ ]

5 × 9 = [ ] × [ ] = [ ]   2 × 3 = [ ] × [ ] = [ ]

B

2 × 12 = [ ] × [ ] = [ ]   2 × 8 = [16]   2 × 50 = [ ]

10 × 3 = [ ] × [ ] = [ ]   10 × 6 = [ ]   10 × 11 = [ ]

5 × 8 = [ ] × [ ] = [ ]   5 × 4 = [ ]   5 × 12 = [ ]

2 × 9 = [ ] × [ ] = [ ]   2 × 7 = [ ]   2 × 20 = [ ]

10 × 12 = [ ] × [ ] = [ ]   10 × 9 = [ ]   10 × 8 = [ ]

5 × 7 = [ ] × [ ] = [ ]   5 × 11 = [ ]   5 × 20 = [ ]

C

2 × 30 = [ ]   3 × 9 = [ ]   4 × 6 = [ ]

3 × 6 = [ ]   4 × 8 = [ ]   5 × 50 = [ ]

4 × 7 = [ ]   5 × 90 = [ ]   10 × 20 = [ ]

5 × 40 = [ ]   10 × 18 = [ ]   2 × 25 = [ ]

10 × 50 = [ ]   2 × 60 = [ ]   3 × 8 = [ ]

2 × 14 = [ ]   3 × 7 = [ ]   4 × 9 = [ ]

Colour the fraction shown.

A

 $\frac{1}{4}$

 $\frac{1}{3}$

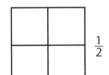 $\frac{1}{4}$

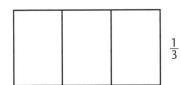 $\frac{1}{2}$

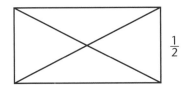 $\frac{1}{3}$

 $\frac{1}{2}$

B

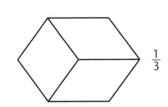 $\frac{1}{3}$

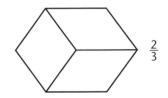 $\frac{2}{3}$

 $\frac{1}{4}$

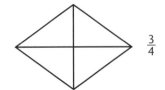 $\frac{3}{4}$

 $\frac{1}{3}$

 $\frac{2}{4}$

C

 $\frac{1}{5}$

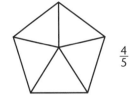 $\frac{4}{5}$

 $\frac{3}{8}$

 $\frac{5}{8}$

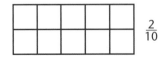 $\frac{2}{10}$

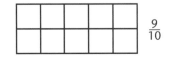 $\frac{9}{10}$

A

Colour the squares
half – blue
quarter – red

$\frac{1}{2}$ of 24 ☐

$\frac{1}{4}$ of 24 ☐

$\frac{1}{2}$ of 32 ☐

$\frac{1}{4}$ of 32 ☐

Colour $\frac{1}{3}$ blue.

$\frac{1}{3}$ of 15 ☐

$\frac{1}{3}$ of 24 ☐

B

Find one half of:

6 ☐

14 ☐

22 ☐

100 ☐

60 ☐

Find one quarter of:

36 ☐

12 ☐

28 ☐

16 ☐

80 ☐

Find one third of:

12 ☐

30 ☐

18 ☐

9 ☐

21 ☐

C

Find one fifth of:

10 ☐

35 ☐

50 ☐

25 ☐

100 ☐

Find one tenth of:

40 ☐

100 ☐

70 ☐

500 ☐

90 ☐

Find one sixth of:

12 ☐

24 ☐

60 ☐

18 ☐

36 ☐

Write the number shown in the box.

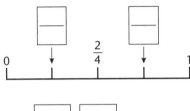

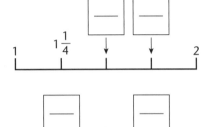

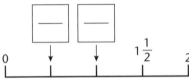

B

Count on in quarters from:

2	$2\frac{1}{4}$			3
0				1
$8\frac{3}{4}$				
$3\frac{1}{4}$				
$5\frac{1}{2}$				

Count on in halves from:

0				2
$1\frac{1}{2}$				
4				
$6\frac{1}{2}$				
8				

C

Write the fraction shown by the letters.

A .... B ....   E .... F ....   I .... J ....

C .... D ....   G .... H ....   K .... L ....

Write the missing number. Use the three given numbers only.

A

7 + 5 = ☐12

5 + 7 = ☐

12 − 5 = ☐

12 − 7 = ☐

15 − 9 = 6

15 − ☐ = ☐

☐ − ☐ = 15

☐ − ☐ = ☐

42 + 10 = ☐

☐ + ☐ = ☐

☐ − ☐ = ☐

☐ − ☐ = ☐

27 − 10 = ☐

☐ − ☐ = ☐

☐ + ☐ = ☐

☐ + ☐ = ☐

B

38 + 9 = ☐

☐ + ☐ = ☐

☐ − ☐ = ☐

☐ − ☐ = ☐

64 − 6 = ☐

☐ − ☐ = ☐

☐ + ☐ = ☐

☐ + ☐ = ☐

59 + 40 = ☐

☐ + ☐ = ☐

☐ − ☐ = ☐

☐ − ☐ = ☐

83 − 20 = ☐

☐ − ☐ = ☐

☐ + ☐ = ☐

☐ + ☐ = ☐

C

146 + ☐ = 153

☐ + ☐ = ☐

☐ − ☐ = ☐

☐ − ☐ = ☐

62 − ☐ = 37

☐ − ☐ = ☐

☐ + ☐ = ☐

☐ + ☐ = ☐

281 + ☐ = 331

☐ + ☐ = ☐

☐ − ☐ = ☐

☐ − ☐ = ☐

☐ − 30 = 375

☐ − ☐ = ☐

☐ + ☐ = ☐

☐ + ☐ = ☐

Fill in the boxes.

A

$6 + 9 = 15$

$8 + \boxed{} = 20$

$\boxed{} + 7 = 11$

$9 + \boxed{} = 14$

$\boxed{} - 8 = 7$

$19 - \boxed{} = 12$

$\boxed{} - 9 = 3$

$14 - \boxed{} = 8$

$\boxed{} + 10 = 40$

$10 + \boxed{} = 90$

$\boxed{} + 10 = 85$

$10 + \boxed{} = 47$

$\boxed{} - 10 = 31$

$56 - \boxed{} = 10$

$\boxed{} - 10 = 54$

$29 - \boxed{} = 10$

B

$\boxed{} + 7 = 95$

$25 + \boxed{} = 33$

$\boxed{} + 4 = 101$

$59 + \boxed{} = 65$

$\boxed{} - 8 = 63$

$33 - \boxed{} = 29$

$\boxed{} - 7 = 55$

$96 - \boxed{} = 87$

$\boxed{} + 20 = 70$

$60 + \boxed{} = 100$

$\boxed{} + 35 = 75$

$30 + \boxed{} = 98$

$\boxed{} - 50 = 40$

$70 - \boxed{} = 40$

$\boxed{} - 70 = 14$

$95 - \boxed{} = 40$

C

$\boxed{} + 9 = 266$

$474 + \boxed{} = 482$

$\boxed{} + 3 = 732$

$398 + \boxed{} = 404$

$\boxed{} - 7 = 597$

$240 - \boxed{} = 235$

$\boxed{} - 9 = 556$

$832 - \boxed{} = 824$

$\boxed{} + 30 = 300$

$450 + \boxed{} = 510$

$\boxed{} + 90 = 333$

$576 + \boxed{} = 626$

$\boxed{} - 70 = 660$

$360 - \boxed{} = 280$

$\boxed{} - 40 = 767$

$932 - \boxed{} = 842$

Fill in the box.

A

6 blue marbles

7 red marbles

[ ] marbles altogether

20 thick paint brushes

5 fewer thin brushes

[ ] thin brushes

16 sausages

7 are eaten

[ ] sausages left

12 boys

10 girls

[ ] children

B

27 children in 2T

14 are girls

[ ] are boys

60 cans in a shop

7 are bought

[ ] cans are left

Jason has 55p.

Jill has 20p.

They have [ ] p altogether.

29 fish in one pond

5 more in a second pond

[ ] fish in the second pond

C

36 books on the top shelf

28 on the bottom shelf

[ ] books altogether

Cheese weighs 245 g

80 g is used

[ ] g is left

A toy costs 59p.

I pay £1.

I am given [ ] p change.

There are 157 trees in a wood.

12 more are planted

[ ] trees in the wood

Complete the tally charts.

A

The favourite pets of 24 children.

H   D   ⊄   D   H   S   D   ⊄

D   H   D   ⊄   S   H   ⊄   H

⊄   S   D   H   D   ⊄   H   D

Pet	Tally	Total
cat	⊞ I	6
dog		
hamster		
snake		

B

How 32 children come to school.

C   B   W   W   B   C   W   S

B   W   C   S   W   B   B   W

B   W   B   C   S   W   W   B

W   B   C   W   B   W   B   C

Way	Tally	Total
bike		
car		
scooter		
walk		

C

The colours of 50 flowers in a display.

W   P   Y   R   Y   P   W   Y   P   W

Y   Y   W   P   Y   W   R   P   Y   Y

P   Y   R   W   P   Y   P   P   W   P

W   R   P   Y   W   P   R   Y   P   W

P   Y   Y   R   P   W   Y   W   P   Y

Colour	Tally	Total
pink		
red		
white		
yellow		

A

Breakfast	People
beans	3
cereal	8
eggs	5
smoothie	4
toast	7

How many people?

toast ☐

beans ☐

smoothie ☐

eggs ☐

cereal ☐

Which breakfast?

5 people ....

4 people ....

7 people ....

8 people ....

3 people ....

B

Weather	Days
cloud	9
fog	2
sun	12
rain	7

☐ days were sunny.

2 days had ....

☐ more days of cloud than rain.

5 fewer days of rain than ....

☐ days had cloud or rain.

☐ days in month altogether.

C

Day	Ducks
Monday	15
Tuesday	7
Wednesday	21
Thursday	13
Friday	18

☐ ducks on the pond on Wednesday.

☐ more ducks on Monday than Tuesday.

☐ fewer ducks on Thursday than Friday.

☐ ducks on the first 2 days altogether.

☐ ducks altogether on the 5 days.

Fill in the boxes. Use the same three numbers.

A

7 × 2 = ☐

2 × 7 = ☐

14 ÷ 2 = ☐

14 ÷ 7 = ☐

3 × 5 = ☐

5 × 3 = ☐

☐ ÷ 5 = ☐

☐ ÷ 3 = ☐

9 × 10 = ☐

10 × 9 = ☐

☐ ÷ 10 = ☐

☐ ÷ 9 = ☐

6 × 2 = ☐

2 × 6 = ☐

☐ ÷ 2 = ☐

☐ ÷ 6 = ☐

B

11 × 2 = ☐

☐ ÷ 2 = ☐

7 × 5 = ☐

☐ ÷ 5 = 7

12 × 10 = ☐

☐ ÷ 10 = ☐

8 × 2 = ☐

☐ ÷ 2 = ☐

55 ÷ 11 = ☐

☐ × 11 = ☐

60 ÷ 10 = ☐

☐ × 10 = ☐

24 ÷ ☐ = 2

☐ × 2 = ☐

45 ÷ ☐ = 5

☐ × 5 = ☐

C

70 × 2 = ☐

☐ ÷ 2 = ☐

60 × 5 = ☐

☐ ÷ 5 = ☐

350 ÷ 10 = ☐

☐ × 10 = ☐

24 ÷ 4 = ☐

☐ × 4 = ☐

90 × 2 = ☐

☐ ÷ 2 = ☐

80 × 5 = ☐

☐ ÷ 5 = ☐

270 ÷ 10 = ☐

☐ × 10 = ☐

27 ÷ 3 = ☐

☐ × 3 = ☐

Fill in the box.

A

How much is

three 10p coins?

Answer ☐ p.

12 pencils.

2 packets.

☐ pencils in each packet.

2 birds in each nest.

5 nests.

☐ birds altogether.

3 toys cost 60p altogether.

How much does one toy cost?

Answer ☐ p.

B

How many pairs can be made

from 26 children?

Answer ☐ pairs.

Nine sweets in each bag.

5 bags.

☐ sweets altogether.

One spoonful is 10 ml.

Ten spoonfuls.

☐ ml altogether.

I have 5p coins only.

I have 30p altogether.

I have ☐ coins.

C

12 months in one year.

3 years is ☐ months.

2 drinks cost 70p altogether.

How much does one drink cost?

Answer ☐ p.

6 plates in each pile.

4 piles.

☐ plates altogether.

200 g on a scale.

Four weights only.

Each weight is ☐ g.

A

How many minutes are shown by the minute hand of each clock face.

 **15**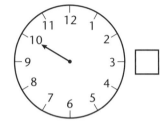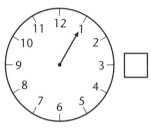

   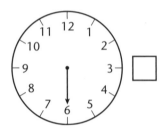   

B

Draw the minute on each clock to show the number of minutes.

 15   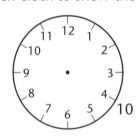 10    60    45

 55    35    25   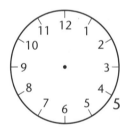 5

C

How many minutes are there in:

1 hour		half an hour	
2 hours		a quarter of an hour	
10 hours		three quarters of an hour	
5 hours		one and a half hours	
4 hours		two and a half hours	

How many minutes pass if the minute hand moves:

from 3 to 7

from 11 to 2

from 4 to 11

from 10 to 8

Write the time in figures.

A

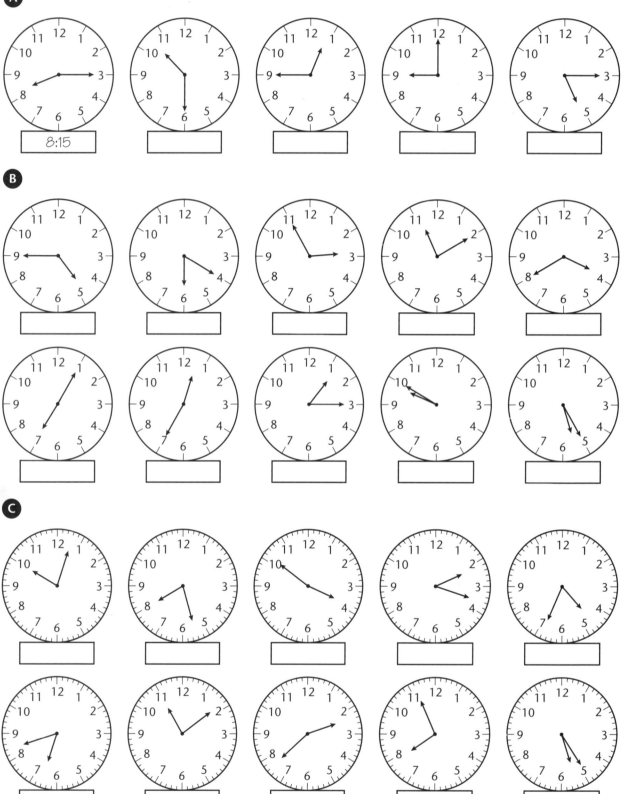

8:15